Ford Diesel Engine Owners Workshop Manual

I M Coomber

Models covered

This manual covers the Ford 2112 cc (2.1 litre), 2304 cc
(2.3 litre) and 2498 cc (2.5 litre) Diesel engines (including
2.5 Turbo) used in the Ford Sierra and Ford Granada

*Does not cover 1.8 litre Turbo Diesel engine used in Sierra and P100
models from January 1990*

(1606-7T1)   ABCDE
FGHIJ
KL

Haynes Publishing Group
Sparkford Nr Yeovil
Somerset BA22 7JJ England

Haynes Publications, Inc
861 Lawrence Drive
Newbury Park
California 91320 USA

Acknowledgements

Thanks are due to Duckhams Oils, who provided lubrication data. Certain illustrations are the copyright of the Ford Motor Company, and are used with their permission. Thanks are also due to Sykes-Pickavant who supplied some of the workshop tools, and to all those people at Sparkford who helped in the production of this Manual.

A book in the **Haynes Owners Workshop Manual Series**

Printed by J. H. Haynes & Co. Ltd., Sparkford, Nr Yeovil, Somerset BA22 7JJ, England

ISBN 1 85010 606 1

British Library Cataloguing in Publication Data
Coomber, Ian *1943* —
    Ford 2.1, 2.3 & 2.5 diesel engine owners workshop manual.
    1. Cars. Maintenance & repair
    I. Title II. Series
    629.28722
    ISBN 1-85010-606-1

Restoring and Preserving our Motoring Heritage

Few people can have had the luck to realise their dreams to quite the same extent and in such a remarkable fashion as John Haynes, Founder and Chairman of the Haynes Publishing Group.

Since 1965 his unique approach to workshop manual publishing has proved so successful that millions of Haynes Manuals are now sold every year throughout the world, covering literally thousands of different makes and models of cars, vans and motorcycles.

A continuing passion for cars and motoring led to the founding in 1985 of a Charitable Trust dedicated to the restoration and preservation of our motoring heritage. To inaugurate the new Museum, John Haynes donated virtually his entire private collection of 52 cars.

Now with an unrivalled international collection of over 210 veteran, vintage and classic cars and motorcycles, the Haynes Motor Museum in Somerset is well on the way to becoming one of the most interesting Motor Museums in the world.

A 70 seat video cinema, a cafe and an extensive motoring bookshop, together with a specially constructed one kilometre motor circuit, make a visit to the Haynes Motor Museum a truly unforgettable experience.

Every vehicle in the museum is preserved in as near as possible mint condition and each car is run every six months on the motor circuit.

Enjoy the picnic area set amongst the rolling Somerset hills. Peer through the William Morris workshop windows at cars being restored, and browse through the extensive displays of fascinating motoring memorabilia.

From the 1903 Oldsmobile through such classics as an MG Midget to the mighty 'E' Type Jaguar, Lamborghini, Ferrari Berlinetta Boxer, and Graham Hill's Lola Cosworth, there is something for everyone, young and old alike, at this Somerset Museum.

Haynes Motor Museum

Situated mid-way between London and Penzance, the Haynes Motor Museum is located just off the A303 at Sparkford, Somerset (home of the Haynes Manual) and is open to the public 7 days a week all year round, except Christmas Day and Boxing Day.

Contents

About this manual

Its aim

The aim of this manual is to help you get the best value from your vehicle. It can do so in several ways. It can help you decide what work must be done (even should you choose to get it done by a garage), provide information on routine maintenance and servicing, and give a logical course of action and diagnosis when random faults occur. However, it is hoped that you will use the manual by tackling the work yourself. On simpler jobs it may even be quicker than booking the car into a garage and going there twice, to leave and collect it. Perhaps most important, a lot of money can be saved by avoiding the costs a garage must charge to cover its labour and overheads.

The manual has drawings and descriptions to show the function of the various components so that their layout can be understood. Then the tasks are described and photographed in a step-by-step sequence so that even a novice can do the work.

Unlike most Haynes manuals, which cover a particular vehicle in different trim levesl and engine sizes, this book covers one engine and its associated equipment as fitted to a range of vehicles. Items which are common to Diesel and petrol models - eg bodywork, transmission and running gear - are not covered in this book. For such items, the reader is advised to refer to the model-specific manual appropriate to his/her car - see rear cover of this manual.

Its arrangement

The manual is divided into eight Chapters, each covering a logical sub-division of the vehicle. The Chapters are each divided into Sections, numbered with single figures, eg 5; and the Sections into paragraphs (or sub-sections), with decimal numbers following on from the Section they are in, eg 5.1, 5.2, 5.3 etc.

It is freely illustrated, especially in those parts where there is a detailed sequence of operations to be carried out. There are two forms of illustration: figures and photographs. The figures are numbered in sequence with decimal numbers, according to their position in the Chapter - eg Fig. 6.4 is the fourth drawing/illustration in Chapter 6. Photographs carry the same number (either individually or in related groups) as the Section or sub-section to which they relate.

There is an alphabetical index at the back of the manual as well as a contents list at the front. Each Chapter is also preceded by its own individual contents list.

References to the 'left' or 'right' of the vehicle are in the sense of a person in the driver's seat facing forwards.

Unless otherwise stated, nuts and bolts are removed by turning anti-clockwise, and tightened by turning clockwise.

Vehicle manufacturers continually make changes to specifications and recommendations, and these, when notified, are incorporated into our manuals at the earliest opportunity.

Whilst every care is taken to ensure that the information in this manual is correct, no liability can be accepted by the authors or publishers for loss, damage or injury caused by any errors in, or omissions from, the information given.

Introduction to the Ford 2.1, 2.3 and 2.5 litre Diesel engines

The Ford Diesel engines covered in this manual are of 2.1, 2.3 and 2.5 litre capacity. The 2.1 litre engine was first fitted to the Granada model in 1977. The same Granada model was later fitted with the 2.5 litre capacity engine. The new Granada model produced from March 1986 is fitted with the latest version of the 2.5 litre engine. The Sierra Diesel engine is of 2.3 litre capacity and this was first introduced in October of 1982.

All engines are similar in design, being mounted in-line, and are of four-cylinder, overhead valve type with water-cooling. The 2.1 litre engine differs in having 'wet' cylinder liners, whilst the 2.3 and 2.5 litre engines have the cylinders machined direct to the block.

A turbocharged version of the 2.5 litre engine replaced the normally aspirated unit in the Granada model from December 1988.

The main advantages of the Diesel engine are increased fuel economy and longer engine life when compared with the petrol equivalent.

Routine maintenance tasks are few and are easily carried out, although some jobs will require the purchase or construction of special tools. The fuel injection pump unit is not use-serviceable, but all major items of the fuel injection system can be removed for replacement or servicing (where required). Compared with a spark ignition system (used on petrol engines) the diesel equipment is virtually maintenance-free.

Outside the engine bay, the vehicles to which the engine is fitted are much the same in both Diesel and petrol versions. For complete coverage of a particular vehicle, the appropriate manual for the petrol engine model concerned will be required as well.

General dimensions, weights and capacities

Dimensions
Overall length:
Sierra (Hatchback)	4407 mm (173.5 in)
Sierra (Saloon)	4468 mm (176.0 in)
Sierra (Estate)	4470 mm (176.0 in)
Granada (Saloon) – up to 1981	4633 mm (182.4 in)
Granada (Estate) – up to 1981	4752 mm (187.1 in)
Granada (Saloon) – 1982 to 1985	4679 mm (184.2 in)
Granada (Estate) – 1982 to 1985	4767 mm (188.9 in)
Granada – 1986 on	4669 mm (183.8 in)

Overall width:
Sierra (Hatchback)	1720 mm (67.7 in)
Sierra (Saloon)	1720 mm (67.7 in)
Sierra (Estate)	1730 mm (68.1 in)
Granada – up to 1981	1790 mm (70.5 in)
Granada – 1982 to 1985	1800 mm (70.9 in)
Granada – 1986 on (including mirrors)	1963 mm (77.3 in)

Overall height:
Sierra (Hatchback)	1420 mm (55.9 in)
Sierra (Saloon)	1420 mm (55.9 in)
Sierra (Estate)	1458 mm (57.4 in)
Granada (Saloon) – up to 1981	1378 mm (54.3 in)
Granada (Estate) – up to 1981	1381 mm (54.4 in)
Granada (Saloon) – 1982 to 1985	1416 mm (55.8 in)
Granada (Estate) – 1982 to 1985	1424 mm (56.1 in)
Granada – 1986 on	1425 to 1450 mm (56.1 to 57.1 in)

Wheelbase:
Sierra (all models)	2609 mm (102.7 in)
Granada – up to 1985	2769 mm (109.0 in)
Granada – 1986 on	2743 mm (108.0 in)

Kerb weights
Sierra:
Hatchback L	1170 kg (2580 lb)
Saloon L	1165 kg (2569 lb)
Estate L	1235 kg (2723 lb)
Hatchback GL	1200 kg (2646 lb)
Saloon GL	1200 kg (2646 lb)
Estate GL	1255 kg (2767 lb)

Granada – up to 1985:	2.1 litre	2.5 litre
Saloon L	1380 kg (3042 lb)	1410 kg (3109 lb)
Estate L	–	1470 kg (3241 lb)
Saloon GL	1415 kg (3120 lb)	1415 kg (3120 lb)
Estate GL	–	1490 kg (3285 lb)

Granada – 1986 on:
Taxi, LX and GL	1325 kg (2921 lb)
Ghia	1335 kg (2943 lb)

Towing weights
Maximum allowable trailer nose weight (at coupling):
Granada (up to 1985) and Sierra	50 kg (110 lb)
Granada – 1986 on	75 kg (165 lb)

Capacities (approx)

Engine oil:
    With filter change .... 5.6 litres (9.9 pints)
    Without filter change .... 5.0 litres (8.8 pints)
Cooling system (including heater):
    Sierra .... 9.5 litres (16.7 pints)
    Granada – up to 1985 .... 10.0 litres (17.6 pints)
    Granada – 1986 on .... 11.0 litres (19.4 pints)
Fuel tank:
    Sierra .... 60 litres (13.2 gal)
    Granada Saloon – up to 1985 .... 65 litres (14.3 gal)
    Granada Estate – up to 1985 .... 62 litres (13.6 gal)
    Granada – 1986 on .... 70 litres (15.4 gal)
Transmission oil:
    Sierra .... 1.9 litres (3.3 pints)
    Granada – up to 1985 .... 1.7 litres (3.0 pints)
    Granada – 1986 on .... 1.2 litres (2.1 pints)
Final drive oil:
    Sierra .... 0.8 to 0.9 litre (1.4 to 1.6 pints)
    Granada – up to 1985 .... 1.4 litres (2.5 pints)
    Granada – 1986 on .... 0.9 litre (1.6 pints)
Power steering – all models .... Fill to the 'MAX' mark

Conversion factors

Length (distance)

Inches (in)	X	25.4	= Millimetres (mm)	X 0.0394	= Inches (in)
Feet (ft)	X	0.305	= Metres (m)	X 3.281	= Feet (ft)
Miles	X	1.609	= Kilometres (km)	X 0.621	= Miles

Volume (capacity)

Cubic inches (cu in; in³)	X	16.387	= Cubic centimetres (cc; cm³)	X 0.061	= Cubic inches (cu in; in³)
Imperial pints (Imp pt)	X	0.568	= Litres (l)	X 1.76	= Imperial pints (Imp pt)
Imperial quarts (Imp qt)	X	1.137	= Litres (l)	X 0.88	= Imperial quarts (Imp qt)
Imperial quarts (Imp qt)	X	1.201	= US quarts (US qt)	X 0.833	= Imperial quarts (Imp qt)
US quarts (US qt)	X	0.946	= Litres (l)	X 1.057	= US quarts (US qt)
Imperial gallons (Imp gal)	X	4.546	= Litres (l)	X 0.22	= Imperial gallons (Imp gal)
Imperial gallons (Imp gal)	X	1.201	= US gallons (US gal)	X 0.833	= Imperial gallons (Imp gal)
US gallons (US gal)	X	3.785	= Litres (l)	X 0.264	= US gallons (US gal)

Mass (weight)

Ounces (oz)	X	28.35	= Grams (g)	X 0.035	= Ounces (oz)
Pounds (lb)	X	0.454	= Kilograms (kg)	X 2.205	= Pounds (lb)

Force

Ounces-force (ozf; oz)	X	0.278	= Newtons (N)	X 3.6	= Ounces-force (ozf; oz)
Pounds-force (lbf; lb)	X	4.448	= Newtons (N)	X 0.225	= Pounds-force (lbf; lb)
Newtons (N)	X	0.1	= Kilograms-force (kgf; kg)	X 9.81	= Newtons (N)

Pressure

Pounds-force per square inch (psi; lbf/in²; lb/in²)	X	0.070	= Kilograms-force per square centimetre (kgf/cm²; kg/cm²)	X 14.223	= Pounds-force per square inch (psi; lbf/in²; lb/in²)
Pounds-force per square inch (psi; lbf/in²; lb/in²)	X	0.068	= Atmospheres (atm)	X 14.696	= Pounds-force per square inch (psi; lbf/in²; lb/in²)
Pounds-force per square inch (psi; lbf/in²; lb/in²)	X	0.069	= Bars	X 14.5	= Pounds-force per square inch (psi; lbf/in²; lb/in²)
Pounds-force per square inch (psi; lbf/in²; lb/in²)	X	6.895	= Kilopascals (kPa)	X 0.145	= Pounds-force per square inch (psi; lbf/in²; lb/in²)
Kilopascals (kPa)	X	0.01	= Kilograms-force per square centimetre (kgf/cm²; kg/cm²)	X 98.1	= Kilopascals (kPa)
Millibar (mbar)	X	100	= Pascals (Pa)	X 0.01	= Millibar (mbar)
Millibar (mbar)	X	0.0145	= Pounds-force per square inch (psi; lbf/in²; lb/in²)	X 68.947	= Millibar (mbar)
Millibar (mbar)	X	0.75	= Millimetres of mercury (mmHg)	X 1.333	= Millibar (mbar)
Millibar (mbar)	X	0.401	= Inches of water (inH₂O)	X 2.491	= Millibar (mbar)
Millimetres of mercury (mmHg)	X	0.535	= Inches of water (inH₂O)	X 1.868	= Millimetres of mercury (mmHg)
Inches of water (inH₂O)	X	0.036	= Pounds-force per square inch (psi; lbf/in²; lb/in²)	X 27.68	= Inches of water (inH₂O)

Torque (moment of force)

Pounds-force inches (lbf in; lb in)	X	1.152	= Kilograms-force centimetre (kgf cm; kg cm)	X 0.868	= Pounds-force inches (lbf in; lb in)
Pounds-force inches (lbf in; lb in)	X	0.113	= Newton metres (Nm)	X 8.85	= Pounds-force inches (lbf in; lb in)
Pounds-force inches (lbf in; lb in)	X	0.083	= Pounds-force feet (lbf ft; lb ft)	X 12	= Pounds-force inches (lbf in; lb in)
Pounds-force feet (lbf ft; lb ft)	X	0.138	= Kilograms-force metres (kgf m; kg m)	X 7.233	= Pounds-force feet (lbf ft; lb ft)
Pounds-force feet (lbf ft; lb ft)	X	1.356	= Newton metres (Nm)	X 0.738	= Pounds-force feet (lbf ft; lb ft)
Newton metres (Nm)	X	0.102	= Kilograms-force metres (kgf m; kg m)	X 9.804	= Newton metres (Nm)

Power

Horsepower (hp)	X	745.7	= Watts (W)	X 0.0013	= Horsepower (hp)

Velocity (speed)

Miles per hour (miles/hr; mph)	X	1.609	= Kilometres per hour (km/hr; kph)	X 0.621	= Miles per hour (miles/hr; mph)

Fuel consumption*

Miles per gallon, Imperial (mpg)	X	0.354	= Kilometres per litre (km/l)	X 2.825	= Miles per gallon, Imperial (mpg)
Miles per gallon, US (mpg)	X	0.425	= Kilometres per litre (km/l)	X 2.352	= Miles per gallon, US (mpg)

Temperature

Degrees Fahrenheit = (°C x 1.8) + 32   Degrees Celsius (Degrees Centigrade; °C) = (°F - 32) x 0.56

*It is common practice to convert from miles per gallon (mpg) to litres/100 kilometres (l/100km), where mpg (Imperial) x l/100 km = 282 and mpg (US) x l/100 km = 235

Safety first!

Professional motor mechanics are trained in safe working procedures. However enthusiastic you may be about getting on with the job in hand, do take the time to ensure that your safety is not put at risk. A moment's lack of attention can result in an accident, as can failure to observe certain elementary precautions.

There will always be new ways of having accidents, and the following points do not pretend to be a comprehensive list of all dangers; they are intended rather to make you aware of the risks and to encourage a safety-conscious approach to all work you carry out on your vehicle.

Essential DOs and DON'Ts

DON'T rely on a single jack when working underneath the vehicle. Always use reliable additional means of support, such as axle stands, securely placed under a part of the vehicle that you know will not give way.

DON'T attempt to loosen or tighten high-torque nuts (e.g. wheel hub nuts) while the vehicle is on a jack; it may be pulled off.

DON'T start the engine without first ascertaining that the transmission is in neutral and the parking brake applied.

DON'T suddenly remove the filler cap from a hot cooling system – cover it with a cloth and release the pressure gradually first, or you may get scalded by escaping coolant.

DON'T attempt to drain oil until you are sure it has cooled sufficiently to avoid scalding you.

DON'T grasp any part of the engine or exhaust without first ascertaining that it is sufficiently cool to avoid burning you.

DON'T allow brake fluid or antifreeze to contact vehicle paintwork.

DON'T syphon toxic liquids such as fuel, brake fluid or antifreeze by mouth, or allow them to remain on your skin.

DON'T inhale dust – it may be injurious to health (see *Asbestos* below).

DON'T allow any spilt oil or grease to remain on the floor – wipe it up straight away, before someone slips on it.

DON'T use ill-fitting spanners or other tools which may slip and cause injury.

DON'T attempt to lift a heavy component which may be beyond your capability – get assistance.

DON'T rush to finish a job, or take unverified short cuts.

DON'T allow children or animals in or around an unattended vehicle.

DO wear eye protection when using power tools such as drill, sander, bench grinder etc, and when working under the vehicle.

DO use a barrier cream on your hands prior to undertaking dirty jobs – it will protect your skin from infection as well as making the dirt easier to remove afterwards; but make sure your hands aren't left slippery. Note that long-term contact with used engine oil can be a health hazard.

DO keep loose clothing (cuffs, tie etc) and long hair well out of the way of moving mechanical parts.

DO remove rings, wristwatch etc, before working on the vehicle – especially the electrical system.

DO ensure that any lifting tackle used has a safe working load rating adequate for the job.

DO keep your work area tidy – it is only too easy to fall over articles left lying around.

DO get someone to check periodically that all is well, when working alone on the vehicle.

DO carry out work in a logical sequence and check that everything is correctly assembled and tightened afterwards.

DO remember that your vehicle's safety affects that of yourself and others. If in doubt on any point, get specialist advice.

IF, in spite of following these precautions, you are unfortunate enough to injure yourself, seek medical attention as soon as possible.

Asbestos

Certain friction, insulating, sealing, and other products – such as brake linings, clutch linings, gaskets, etc – contain asbestos. *Extreme care must be taken to avoid inhalation of dust from such products since it is hazardous to health.* If in doubt, assume that they *do* contain asbestos.

Fire

Remember at all times that fuel is highly flammable. Never smoke, or have any kind of naked flame around, when working on the vehicle. But the risk does not end there – a spark caused by an electrical short-circuit, by two metal surfaces contacting each other, by careless use of tools, or even by static electricity built up in your body under certain conditions, can ignite fuel vapour, which in a confined space is highly explosive.

Always disconnect the battery earth (ground) terminal before working on any part of the fuel or electrical system, and never risk spilling fuel on to a hot engine or exhaust.

It is recommended that a fire extinguisher of a type suitable for fuel and electrical fires is kept handy in the garage or workplace at all times.

Note: *Any reference to a 'torch' appearing in this manual should always be taken to mean a hand-held battery-operated electric lamp or flashlight. It does NOT mean a welding/gas torch or blowlamp.*

Fumes

Certain fumes are highly toxic and can quickly cause unconsciousness and even death if inhaled to any extent. Fuel vapour comes into this category, as do the vapours from certain solvents such as trichloroethylene. Any draining or pouring of such volatile fluids should be done in a well ventilated area.

When using cleaning fluids and solvents, read the instructions carefully. Never use materials from unmarked containers – they may give off poisonous vapours.

Never run the engine of a motor vehicle in an enclosed space such as a garage. Exhaust fumes contain carbon monoxide which is extremely poisonous; if you need to run the engine, always do so in the open air or at least have the rear of the vehicle outside the workplace.

If you are fortunate enough to have the use of an inspection pit, never drain or pour fuel, and never run the engine, while the vehicle is standing over it; the fumes, being heavier than air, will concentrate in the pit with possibly lethal results.

The battery

Never cause a spark, or allow a naked light, near the vehicle's battery. It will normally be giving off a certain amount of hydrogen gas, which is highly explosive.

Always disconnect the battery earth (ground) terminal before working on the fuel or electrical systems.

If possible, loosen the filler plugs or cover when charging the battery from an external source. Do not charge at an excessive rate or the battery may burst.

Take care when topping up and when carrying the battery. The acid electrolyte, even when diluted, is very corrosive and should not be allowed to contact the eyes or skin.

If you ever need to prepare electrolyte yourself, always add the acid slowly to the water, and never the other way round. Protect against splashes by wearing rubber gloves and goggles.

When jump starting a car using a booster battery, for negative earth (ground) vehicles, connect the jump leads in the following sequence: First connect one jump lead between the positive (+) terminals of the two batteries. Then connect the other jump lead first to the negative (–) terminal of the booster battery, and then to a good earthing (ground) point on the vehicle to be started, at least 18 in (45 cm) from the battery if possible. Ensure that hands and jump leads are clear of any moving parts, and that the two vehicles do not touch. Disconnect the leads in the reverse order.

Mains electricity and electrical equipment

When using an electric power tool, inspection light etc, always ensure that the appliance is correctly connected to its plug and that, where necessary, it is properly earthed (grounded). Do not use such appliances in damp conditions and, again, beware of creating a spark or applying excessive heat in the vicinity of fuel or fuel vapour. Also ensure that the appliances meet the relevant national safety standards.

Diesel fuel

Diesel injection pumps supply fuel at very high pressure, and extreme care must be taken when working on the fuel injectors and fuel pipes. It is advisable to place an absorbent cloth around the union before slackening a fuel pipe, and *never expose the hands or any part of the body to injector spray, as the high working pressure can cause the fuel to penetrate the skin, with possibly fatal results.*

Jacking, towing and wheel changing

Jacking

Use the jack supplied with the vehicle only for wheel changing during roadside emergencies (photos). Chock the wheel diagonally opposite the one being removed.

When raising the vehicle for repair or maintenance, preferably use a trolley or hydraulic jack with a wooden block as an insulator to prevent damage to the underbody. Place the jack under a structural member at the points indicated, never raise the vehicle by jacking up under the engine sump or transmission casing. If both front or both rear wheels are to be raised, jack up one side first and securely support it on an axle stand before raising the other side.

To avoid repetition, the procedures for raising the vehicle in order to carry out work under it is not included before each relevant operation described in this manual.

It is to be preferred and is certainly recommended that the vehicle is positioned over an inspection pit or raised on a lift. When such equipment is not available, use ramps or jack up the vehicle as previously described, but always supplement the lifting device with axle stands.

Towing

Towing eyes are provided at both front and rear of the vehicle (photos). The rear towing eye should be used only for emergency towing of another vehicle; for trailer towing a properly fitted towing bracket is required.

When being towed, insert the ignition key and turn it to position 11. This will unlock the steering, allow the lights and direction indicators to be used and activate the braking system.

It should be noted that the car cannot be tow-started. This is due to the cold-start system only being activated when the engine is cranked over on the starter motor. In this instance, it will be necessary to use battery jump leads and a second battery.

Wheel changing

Park on a firm flat surface if possible. Apply the handbrake and engage reverse gear. Chock the wheel diagonally opposite the one being removed.

Jack location – Granada up to 1985

Jack location (front) – Sierra

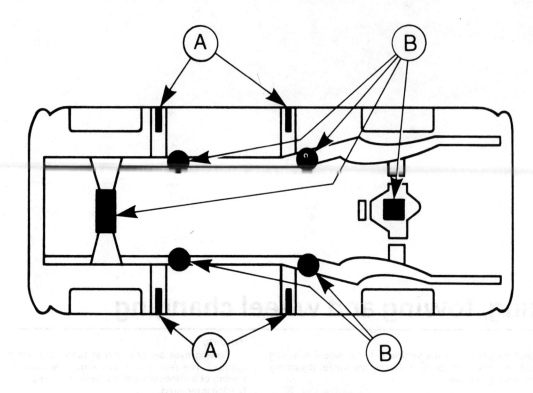

Vehicle support points – Granada up to 1985

A   *Wheel changing jack*   B   *Workshop jack*

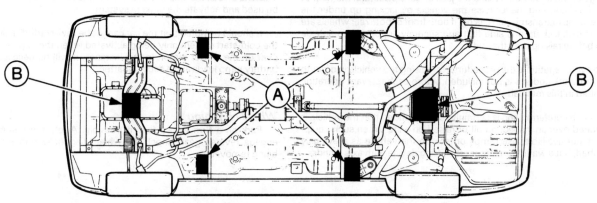

Vehicle support points – Sierra

A   *Jacking and support points*   B   *Trolley jack lift points*

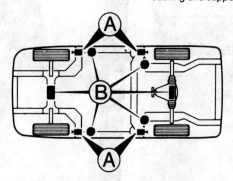

Vehicle support points – Granada 1983 on

A   *Wheel changing jack*   B   *Trolley jack or axle stands*

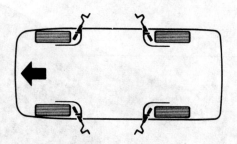

Swivel jack in each alternative position when lifting the Granada (1986 on)

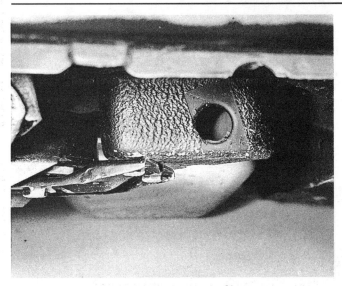

Jack location point (rear) – Sierra

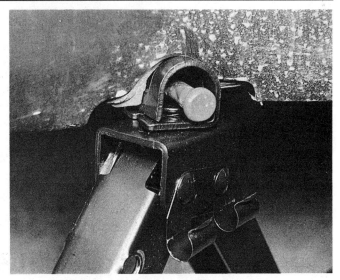

Jack engagement point – Granada 1986 on

Using an axle stand (Sierra shown)

Front towing eye (Granada 1986 on shown)

Remove the wheel trim, when applicable, for access to the wheel nuts. Prise the trim off if necessary using the plastic-tipped end of the wheelbrace. Use the other end of the wheelbrace to slacken each wheel nut by half a turn.

If the car is fairly new, the wheels and tyres will have been balanced on the vehicle during production. To maintain this relationship, mark the position of the wheel relative to the hub. (This is not necessary if the tyre is to be removed for repair or renewal, since the balance will inevitably be altered.)

Jack up the vehicle until the wheel is clear of the ground. Remove the wheel nuts and lift the wheel off the stands. Transfer the wheel centre cap on alloy wheels, then fit the new wheel onto the studs and secure it with the nuts. Tighten the nuts until they are snug, but do not tighten them fully yet.

Lower the vehicle and remove the jack. Carry out the final tightening of the wheel nuts in criss-cross sequence. The use of a torque wrench is strongly recommended, especially when light alloy wheels are fitted. See Chapter 7 Specifications for the recommended tightening torque.

Refit the wheel trim, when applicable, and stow the tools, if a new wheel has been brought into service, have it balanced on the vehicle if necessary.

Rear towing eye (Granada 1986 on shown)

Tools and working facilities

Introduction

A selection of good tools is a fundamental requirement for anyone contemplating the maintenance and repair of a motor vehicle. For the owner who does not possess any, their purchase will prove a considerable expense, offsetting some of the savings made by doing-it-yourself. However, provided that the tools purchased meet the relevant national safety standards and are of good quality, they will last for many years and prove an extremely worthwhile investment.

To help the average owner to decide which tools are needed to carry out the various tasks detailed in this manual, we have compiled three lists of tools under the following headings: *Maintenance and minor repair, Repair and overhaul,* and *Special.* The newcomer to practical mechanics should start off with the *Maintenance and minor repair* tool kit and confine himself to the simpler jobs around the vehicle. Then, as his confidence and experience grow, he can undertake more difficult tasks, buying extra tools as, and when, they are needed. In this way, a *Maintenance and minor repair* tool kit can be built-up into a *Repair and overhaul* tool kit over a considerable period of time without any major cash outlays. The experienced do-it-yourselfer will have a tool kit good enough for most repair and overhaul procedures and will add tools from the *Special* category when he feels the expense is justified by the amount of use to which these tools will be put.

It is obviously not possible to cover the subject of tools fully here. For those who wish to learn more about tools and their use there is a book entitled *How to Choose and Use Car Tools* available from the publishers of this manual.

Maintenance and minor repair tool kit

The tools given in this list should be considered as a minimum requirement if routine maintenance, servicing and minor repair operations are to be undertaken. We recommend the purchase of combination spanners (ring one end, open-ended the other); although more expensive than open-ended ones, they do give the advantages of both types of spanner.

> *Combination spanners - 10, 11, 12, 13, 14 & 17 mm*
> *Adjustable spanner - 9 inch*
> *Engine sump/gearbox/rear axle drain plug key*
> *Set of feeler gauges*
> *Brake bleed nipple spanner*
> *Screwdriver - 4 in long x $\frac{1}{4}$ in dia (flat blade)*
> *Screwdriver - 4 in long x $\frac{1}{4}$ in dia (cross blade)*
> *Combination pliers - 6 inch*
> *Hacksaw (junior)*
> *Tyre pump*
> *Tyre pressure gauge*
> *Oil can*
> *Fine emery cloth (1 sheet)*
> *Wire brush (small)*
> *Funnel (medium size)*

Repair and overhaul tool kit

These tools are virtually essential for anyone undertaking any major repairs to a motor vehicle, and are additional to those given in the *Maintenance and minor repair* list. Included in this list is a comprehensive set of sockets. Although these are expensive they will be found invaluable as they are so versatile - particularly if various drives are included in the set. We recommend the $\frac{1}{2}$ in square-drive type, as this can be used with most proprietary torque wrenches. If you cannot afford a socket set, even bought piecemeal, then inexpensive tubular box spanners are a useful alternative.

The tools in this list will occasionally need to be supplemented by tools from the *Special* list.

> *Sockets (or box spanners) to cover range in previous list*
> *Reversible ratchet drive (for use with sockets)*
> *Extension piece, 10 inch (for use with sockets)*
> *Universal joint (for use with sockets)*
> *Torque wrench (for use with sockets)*
> *'Mole' wrench - 8 inch*
> *Ball pein hammer*
> *Soft-faced hammer, plastic or rubber*
> *Screwdriver - 6 in long x $\frac{5}{16}$ in dia (flat blade)*
> *Screwdriver - 2 in long x $\frac{5}{16}$ in square (flat blade)*
> *Screwdriver - 1$\frac{1}{2}$ in long x $\frac{1}{4}$ in dia (cross blade)*
> *Screwdriver - 3 in long x $\frac{1}{8}$ in dia (electrician's)*
> *Pliers - electrician's side cutters*
> *Pliers - needle nosed*
> *Pliers - circlip (internal and external)*
> *Cold chisel - $\frac{1}{2}$ inch*
> *Scriber*
> *Scraper*
> *Centre punch*
> *Pin punch*
> *Hacksaw*
> *Valve grinding tool*
> *Steel rule/straight-edge*
> *Allen keys (inc. splined/Torx type if necessary)*
> *Selection of files*
> *Wire brush (large)*
> *Axle-stands*
> *Jack (strong trolley or hydraulic type)*

Special tools

The tools in this list are those which are not used regularly, are expensive to buy, or which need to be used in accordance with their manufacturers' instructions. Unless relatively difficult mechanical jobs are undertaken frequently, it will not be economic to buy many of these tools. Where this is the case, you could consider clubbing together with friends (or joining a motorists' club) to make a joint purchase, or borrowing the tools against a deposit from a local garage or tool hire specialist.

The following list contains only those tools and instruments freely available to the public, and not those special tools produced by the vehicle manufacturer specifically for its dealer network. You will find occasional references to these manufacturers' special tools in the text of this manual. Generally, an alternative method of doing the job without the vehicle manufacturers' special tool is given. However, sometimes, there is no alternative to using them. Where this is the case and the relevant tool cannot be bought or borrowed, you will have to entrust the work to a franchised garage.

Valve spring compressor (where applicable)
Piston ring compressor
Balljoint separator
Universal hub/bearing puller
Impact screwdriver
Micrometer and/or vernier gauge
Dial gauge
Tachometer
Universal electrical multi-meter
Cylinder compression gauge
Lifting tackle
Trolley jack
Light with extension lead

Buying tools

For practically all tools, a tool factor is the best source since he will have a very comprehensive range compared with the average garage or accessory shop. Having said that, accessory shops often offer excellent quality tools at discount prices, so it pays to shop around.

There are plenty of good tools around at reasonable prices, but always aim to purchase items which meet the relevant national safety standards. If in doubt, ask the proprietor or manager of the shop for advice before making a purchase.

Care and maintenance of tools

Having purchased a reasonable tool kit, it is necessary to keep the tools in a clean serviceable condition. After use, always wipe off any dirt, grease and metal particles using a clean, dry cloth, before putting the tools away. Never leave them lying around after they have been used. A simple tool rack on the garage or workshop wall, for items such as screwdrivers and pliers is a good idea. Store all normal wrenches and sockets in a metal box. Any measuring instruments, gauges, meters, etc, must be carefully stored where they cannot be damaged or become rusty.

Take a little care when tools are used. Hammer heads inevitably become marked and screwdrivers lose the keen edge on their blades from time to time. A little timely attention with emery cloth or a file will soon restore items like this to a good serviceable finish.

Working facilities

Not to be forgotten when discussing tools, is the workshop itself. If anything more than routine maintenance is to be carried out, some form of suitable working area becomes essential.

It is appreciated that many an owner mechanic is forced by circumstances to remove an engine or similar item, without the benefit of a garage or workshop. Having done this, any repairs should always be done under the cover of a roof.

Wherever possible, any dismantling should be done on a clean, flat workbench or table at a suitable working height.

Any workbench needs a vice: one with a jaw opening of 4 in (100 mm) is suitable for most jobs. As mentioned previously, some clean dry storage space is also required for tools, as well as for lubricants, cleaning fluids, touch-up paints and so on, which become necessary.

Another item which may be required, and which has a much more general usage, is an electric drill with a chuck capacity of at least $\frac{5}{16}$ in (8 mm). This, together with a good range of twist drills, is virtually essential for fitting accessories such as mirrors and reversing lights.

Last, but not least, always keep a supply of old newspapers and clean, lint-free rags available, and try to keep any working area as clean as possible.

Spanner jaw gap comparison table

Jaw gap (in)	Spanner size
0.250	$\frac{1}{4}$ in AF
0.276	7 mm
0.313	$\frac{5}{16}$ in AF
0.315	8 mm
0.344	$\frac{11}{32}$ in AF; $\frac{1}{8}$ in Whitworth
0.354	9 mm
0.375	$\frac{3}{8}$ in AF
0.394	10 mm
0.433	11 mm
0.438	$\frac{7}{16}$ in AF
0.445	$\frac{3}{16}$ in Whitworth; $\frac{1}{4}$ in BSF
0.472	12 mm
0.500	$\frac{1}{2}$ in AF
0.512	13 mm
0.525	1/4 in Whitworth; $\frac{5}{16}$ in BSF
0.551	14 mm
0.563	$\frac{9}{16}$ in AF
0.591	15 mm
0.600	$\frac{5}{16}$ in Whitworth; $\frac{3}{8}$ in BSF
0.625	$\frac{5}{8}$ in AF
0.630	16 mm
0.669	17 mm
0.686	$\frac{11}{16}$ in AF
0.709	18 mm
0.71	$\frac{3}{8}$ in Whitworth; $\frac{7}{16}$ in BSF
0.748	19 mm
0.750	$\frac{3}{4}$ in AF
0.813	$\frac{13}{16}$ in AF
0.820	$\frac{7}{16}$ in Whitworth; $\frac{1}{2}$ in BSF
0.866	22 mm
0.875	$\frac{7}{8}$ in AF
0.920	$\frac{1}{2}$ in Whitworth; $\frac{9}{16}$ in BSF
0.938	$\frac{15}{16}$ in AF
0.945	24 mm
1.000	1 in AF
1.010	$\frac{9}{16}$ in Whitworth; $\frac{5}{8}$ in BSF
1.024	26 mm
1.063	$1\frac{1}{16}$ in AF; 27 mm
1.100	$\frac{5}{8}$ in Whitworth; $\frac{11}{16}$ in BSF
1.125	$1\frac{1}{8}$ in AF
1.181	30 mm
1.200	$\frac{11}{16}$ in Whitworth; $\frac{3}{4}$ in BSF
1.250	$1\frac{1}{4}$ in AF
1.260	32 mm
1.300	$\frac{3}{4}$ in Whitworth; $\frac{7}{8}$ in BSF
1.313	$1\frac{5}{16}$ in AF
1.390	$\frac{13}{16}$ in Whitworth; $\frac{15}{16}$ in BSF
1.417	36 mm
1.438	$1\frac{7}{16}$ in AF
1.480	$\frac{7}{8}$ in Whitworth; 1 in BSF
1.500	$1\frac{1}{2}$ in AF
1.575	40 mm; $1\frac{5}{8}$ in Whitworth
1.614	41 mm
1.625	$1\frac{5}{8}$ in AF
1.670	1 in Whitworth; $1\frac{1}{8}$ in BSF
1.688	$1\frac{11}{16}$ in AF
1.811	46 mm
1.813	$1\frac{13}{16}$ in AF
1.860	$1\frac{1}{8}$ in Whitworth; $1\frac{1}{4}$ in BSF
1.875	$1\frac{7}{8}$ in AF
1.969	50 mm
2.000	2 in AF
2.050	$1\frac{1}{4}$ in Whitworth; $1\frac{3}{8}$ in BSF
2.165	55 mm
2.362	60 mm

General repair procedures

Whenever servicing, repair or overhaul work is carried out on the car or its components, it is necessary to observe the following procedures and instructions. This will assist in carrying out the operation efficiently and to a professional standard of workmanship.

Joint mating faces and gaskets

Where a gasket is used between the mating faces of two components, ensure that it is renewed on reassembly, and fit it dry unless otherwise stated in the repair procedure. Make sure that the mating faces are clean and dry with all traces of old gasket removed. When cleaning a joint face, use a tool which is not likely to score or damage the face, and remove any burrs or nicks with an oilstone or fine file.

Make sure that tapped holes are cleaned with a pipe cleaner, and keep them free of jointing compound if this is being used unless specifically instructed otherwise.

Ensure that all orifices, channels or pipes are clear and blow through them, preferably using compressed air.

Oil seals

Whenever an oil seal is removed from its working location, either individually or as part of an assembly, it should be renewed.

The very fine sealing lip of the seal is easily damaged and will not seal if the surface it contacts is not completely clean and free from scratches, nicks or grooves. If the original sealing surface of the component cannot be restored, the component should be renewed.

Protect the lips of the seal from any surface which may damage them in the course of fitting. Use tape or a conical sleeve where possible. Lubricate the seal lips with oil before fitting and, on dual lipped seals, fill the space between the lips with grease.

Unless otherwise stated, oil seals must be fitted with their sealing lips toward the lubricant to be sealed.

Use a tubular drift or block of wood of the appropriate size to install the seal and, if the seal housing is shouldered, drive the seal down to the shoulder. If the seal housing is unshouldered, the seal should be fitted with its face flush with the housing top face.

Screw threads and fastenings

Always ensure that a blind tapped hole is completely free from oil, grease, water or other fluid before installing the bolt or stud. Failure to do this could cause the housing to crack due to the hydraulic action of the bolt or stud as it is screwed in.

When tightening a castellated nut to accept a split pin, tighten the nut to the specified torque, where applicable, and then tighten further to the next split pin hole. Never slacken the nut to align a split pin hole unless stated in the repair procedure.

When checking or retightening a nut or bolt to a specified torque setting, slacken the nut or bolt by a quarter of a turn, and then retighten to the specified setting.

Locknuts, locktabs and washers

Any fastening which will rotate against a component or housing in the course of tightening should always have a washer between it and the relevant component or housing.

Spring or split washers should always be renewed when they are used to lock a critical component such as a big-end bearing retaining nut or bolt.

Locktabs which are folded over to retain a nut or bolt should always be renewed.

Self-locking nuts can be reused in non-critical areas, providing resistance can be felt when the locking portion passes over the bolt or stud thread.

Split pins must always be replaced with new ones of the correct size for the hole.

Special tools

Some repair procedures in this manual entail the use of special tools such as a press, two or three-legged pullers, spring compressors etc. Wherever possible, suitable readily available alternatives to the manufacturer's special tools are described, and are shown in use. In some instances, where no alternative is possible, it has been necessary to resort to the use of a manufacturer's tool and this has been done for reasons of safety as well as the efficient completion of the repair operation. Unless you are highly skilled and have a thorough understanding of the procedure described, never attempt to bypass the use of any special tool when the procedure described specifies its use. Not only is there a very great risk of personal injury, but expensive damage could be caused to the components involved.

Buying spare parts
and vehicle identification numbers

Buying spare parts

Spare parts are available from many sources, for example: Ford garages, other garages and accessory shops, and motor factors. Our advice regarding spare part sources is as follows:

Officially appointed Ford garages – This is the best source for parts which are peculiar to your car and are not generally available (eg complete cylinder heads, internal transmission components, badges, interior trim etc). It is also the only place at which you should buy parts if your vehicle is still under warranty – non-Ford components may invalidate the warranty. To be sure of obtaining the correct parts it will always be necessary to give the storeman your car's vehicle identification number, and if possible, to take the 'old' part along for positive identification. Remember that many parts are available on a factory exchange scheme – any parts returned should always be clean! It obviously makes good sense to go straight to the specialists on your car for this type of part for they are best equipped to supply you.

Other garages and accessory shops – These are often very good places to buy materials and components needed for the maintenance of your car (eg oil filters, bulbs, fanbelts, oils and greases, touch-up paint, filler paste, etc). They also sell general accessories, usually have convenient opening hours, charge lower prices and can often be found not far from home.

Motor factors – Good factors will stock all of the more important components which wear out relatively quickly (eg clutch components, pistons, valves, exhaust systems, brake cylinders/pipes/hoses/seals/shoes and pads etc). Motor factors will often provide new or reconditioned components on a part exchange basis – this can save a considerable amount of money.

Vehicle identification numbers

When ordering spare parts, always give as much information as possible. Quote the car model, year of manufacture, body and engine numbers as appropriate.

The vehicle identification number (VIN) plate is mounted on the front crossmember panel and may be seen once the bonnet is open (photo). Besides the VIN it also carries information on vehicle equipment and permissible loads. The VIN is also stamped into the floor panel to the right of the driver's seat, an inspection cover is provided (photo).

The engine number is stamped on the cylinder block on the left-hand side, directly above the fuel injection pump unit.

Other identification numbers or codes are stamped on major items such as the gearbox, final drive housing. These numbers are unlikely to be needed by the home mechanic.

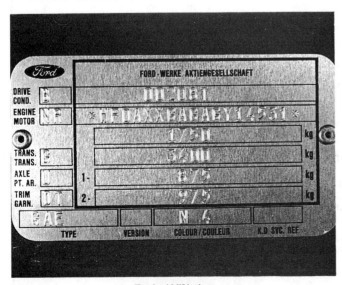

Typical VIN plate

VIN is repeated in recess next to driver's seat

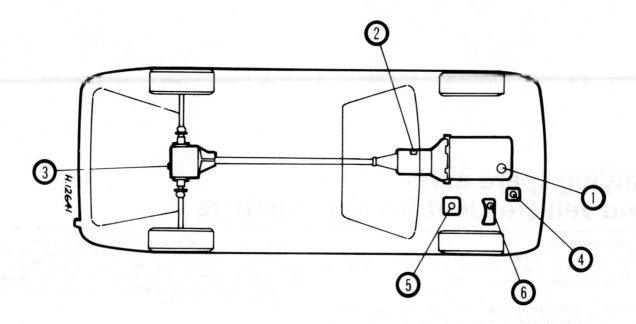

Recommended lubricants and fluids

Component or system	Lubricant type/specification	Duckhams recommendation
1 Engine	Multigrade engine oil, viscosity range SAE 10W/30 to 20W/50, to API SG/CD or better	Duckhams Van Guard, QXR, or Hypergrade
2 Manual gearbox		
4-speed	Gear oil, viscosity SAE 80 EP, to Ford spec SQM-2C 9008-A	Duckhams Hypoid 80
5-speed	Semi-synthetic gear oil, viscosity SAE 80 EP, to Ford spec ESD-M2C 175-A	Duckhams Hypoid 75W/90S
3 Final drive	Hypoid gear oil, viscosity SAE 90 EP to Ford spec SQM-2C 9002-AA or 9003-AA	Duckhams Hypoid 90S
4 Power steering	ATF to Ford spec SQM-2C 9010-A	Duckhams Uni-Matic or D-Matic
5 Brake hydraulic system	Brake fluid to Ford spec Amber SAM-6C 9103-A	Duckhams Universal Brake and Clutch Fluid
6 Cooling system	Soft water and antifreeze to Ford spec SSM-97B 9103-A	Duckhams Universal Antifreeze and Summer Coolant

Routine maintenance

Maintenance is essential for ensuring safety and desirable for the purpose of getting the best in terms of performance and economy from your car. Over the years the need for periodic lubrication – oiling, greasing, and so on – has been drastically reduced if not totally eliminated. This has unfortunately tended to lead some owners to think that because no such action is required, components either no longer exist, or will last for ever. This is certainly not the case; it is essential to carry out regular visual examination as comprehensively as possible in order to spot any possible defects at an early stage before they develop into major expensive repairs.

Every 250 miles (400 km) or weekly – whichever comes first

Engine
Check the engine oil level and top up if necessary
Check the coolant level and top up if necessary

Tyres
Check the tyre pressure and adjust if necessary

Every 6000 miles (10 000 km) – additional

Engine
Clean the oil filler cap in fuel and allow to dry
Check for oil, fuel and water leaks
Check the condition and security of vacuum hoses
Check the condition of drivebelts and adjust tension if necessary
Check the engine oil and renew the oil filter
Check the engine slow running adjustment (adjust slow running mixture only at first 6000 miles/10 000 km)
Check for signs of water in the fuel filter, if necessary drain, prime and bleed the system

Brakes
Check the hydraulic fluid level in the reservoir and top up if necessary. A slight drop due to wear of the disc pads is acceptable but if regular topping up is required the leak should be located and rectified
Check hydraulic lines for leakage
Check servo vacuum hose for condition and security
Check disc pads and rear brake shoes for wear

Tyres
Check tyres for condition and wear
Check wheel nuts for tightness

Bodywork
Check the fluid level in the windscreen washer reservoir and top up if necessary
Check seat belt webbing for cuts, fraying etc.

Every 12 000 miles (20 000 km) – additional

Engine
Check the exhaust system for leaks
Clean battery terminals, check them for tightness, and apply petroleum jelly
Check and if necessary top up the valve clearances

Manual gearbox
Check and if necessary top up the oil level

Driveshafts and final drive
Check the gaiters for condition and security
Check and if necessary top up the final drive oil level

Brakes
Road test and check ABS operation (where fitted)
Check operation of the brake fluid level warning light

Electrical system
Check the operation of all electrical equipment and lights

Suspension and steering
Check all linkages and balljoints for wear and damage
Check and top up the power steering fluid level (where applicable)

Bodywork
Lubricate all hinges and catches
Check the underbody for corrosion and damage

Every 24 000 miles (40 000 km) – additional

Engine
Renew the crankcase emission vent valve
Renew the air filter element
Renew the fuel filter element

Every 36 000 miles (60 000 km) or two years whichever occurs first

Engine
Flush the cooling system and fill with new antifreeze/corrosion inhibitor
Check cooling system pressure cap and seal – renew if necessary

Brakes
Renew the hydraulic brake fluid and check the condition of the visible rubber components of the brake system

Under bonnet view (air cleaner removed) – Sierra

1 Engine oil filler cap
2 VIN plate
3 Brake vacuum pump
4 Washer fluid filler neck

5 Cooling system expansion
   tank
6 Brake master cylinder
   reservoir
7 Fuse box
8 Windscreen wiper motor

9 Injector
10 Battery
11 Suspension strut upper
    mounting
12 Oil filter

13 Fuel filter mounting and
    primer pump
14 Fuel injection pump
15 Thermostat housing
16 Water pump/drive belt
    pulleys

Under bonnet view – **Granada Turbo**

1 VIN plate
2 Alternator
3 Washer fluid filler neck
4 Power steering fluid reservoir

5 Cooling system expansion tank
6 Brake hydraulic fluid reservoir
7 ABS master cylinder and accumulator

8 Engine oil filler
9 Injector
10 Engine oil dipstick
11 Battery
12 ABS valve block

13 Suspension strut upper mounting
14 Air cleaner
15 Fuel injection pump
16 Thermostat
17 Water pump

Underside view of engine (with undershield removed) – Sierra

1 Crankshaft pulley and drivebelts
2 Fuel injection pump
3 Suspension arm
4 Sump
5 Anti-roll bar mounting
6 Transmission
7 Exhaust
8 Front disc brake unit
9 Steering track rod and bellows
10 Alternator
11 Washer fluid reservoir
12 Radiator

Underside view of engine (with undershield removed) – Granada Turbo model

1 Sump
2 Jacking point
3 Transmission
4 Transmission mounting
5 Exhaust system joint and support
6 Anti-roll bar mounting
7 Turbocharger
8 Front disc brake unit
9 Suspension arm
10 Oil cooler hose
11 Power steering pump
12 Cooling fan
13 Steering track rod and bellows

Fault diagnosis

Introduction

The vehicle owner who does his or her own maintenance according to the recommended schedules should not have to use this section of the manual very often. Modern component reliability is such that provided those items subject to wear or deterioration are inspected or renewed at the specified intervals, sudden failure is comparatively rare. Faults do not usually just happen as a result of sudden failure, but develop over a period of time. Major mechanical failures in particular are usually preceded by characteristic symptoms over hundreds or even thousands of miles. Those components which do occasionally fail without warning are often small and easily carried in the vehicle.

With any fault finding, the first step is to decide where to begin investigations. Sometimes this is obvious, but on other occasions a little detective work will be necessary. The owner who makes half a dozen haphazard adjustments or replacements may be successful in curing a fault (or its symptoms), but he will be none the wiser if the fault recurs and he may well have spent more time and money than was necessary. A calm and logical approach will be found to be more satisfactory in the long run. Always take into account any warning signs or abnormalities that may have been noticed in the period preceding the fault – power loss, high or low gauge readings, unusual noises or smells, etc – and remember that failure of components such as fuses may only be pointers to some underlying fault.

The pages which follow here are intended to help in cases of failure to start or breakdown on the road. There is also a Fault Diagnosis Section at the end of each Chapter which should be consulted if the preliminary checks prove unfruitful. Whatever the fault, certain basic principles apply. These are as follows:

Verify the fault. This is simply a matter of being sure that you know what the symptoms are before starting work. This is particularly important if you are investigating a fault for someone else who may not have described it very accurately.

Don't overlook the obvious. For example, if the vehicle won't start, is there fuel in the tank? (Don't take anyone else's word on this particular point, and don't trust the fuel gauge either!) If an electrical fault is indicated, look for loose or broken wires before digging out the test gear.

Cure the disease, not the symptom. Substituting a flat battery with a fully charged one will get you off the hard shoulder, but if the underlying cause is not attended to, the new battery will go the same way.

Don't take anything for granted. Particularly, don't forget that a 'new' component may itself be defective (especially if it's been rattling round in the boot for months), and don't leave components out of a fault diagnosis sequence just because they are new or recently fitted. When you do finally diagnose a difficult fault, you'll probably realise that all the evidence was there from the start.

Electrical faults

Electrical faults can be more puzzling than straightforward mechanical failures, but they are no less susceptible to logical analysis if the basic principles of operation are understood. Vehicle electrical wiring exists in extremely unfavourable conditions – heat, vibration and chemical attack – and the first things to look for are loose or corroded connections and broken or chafed wires, especially where the wires pass through holes in the bodywork or are subject to vibration.

All metal-bodied vehicles in current production have one pole of the battery 'earthed', ie connected to the vehicle bodywork, and in nearly all modern vehicles it is the negative (–) terminal. The various electrical components – motors, bulb holders etc – are also connected to earth, either by means of a lead or directly by their mountings. Electric current flows through the component and then back to the battery via the bodywork. If the component mounting is loose or corroded, or if a good path back to the battery is not available, the circuit will be incomplete and malfunction will result. The engine and/or gearbox are also earthed by means of flexible metal straps to the body or subframe; if these straps are loose or missing, starter motor and generator trouble may result.

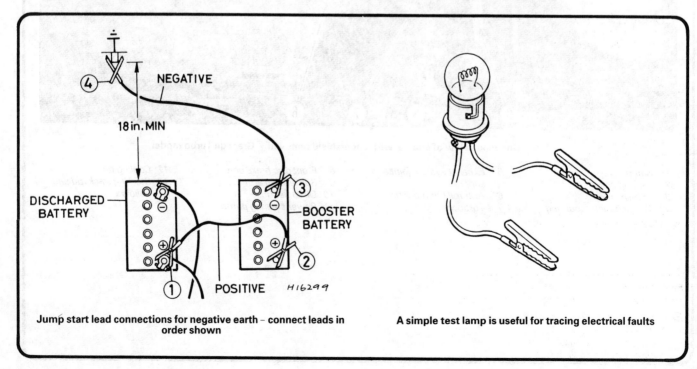

Jump start lead connections for negative earth – connect leads in order shown

A simple test lamp is useful for tracing electrical faults

Assuming the earth return to be satisfactory, electrical faults will be due either to component malfunction or to defects in the current supply. Individual components are dealt with in Chapter 8. If supply wires are broken or cracked internally this results in an open-circuit, and the easiest way to check for this is to bypass the suspect wire temporarily with a length of wire having a crocodile clip or suitable connector at each end. Alternatively, a 12V test lamp can be used to verify the presence of supply voltage at various points along the wire and the break can be thus isolated.

If a bare portion of a live wire touches the bodywork or other earthed metal part, the electricity will take the low-resistance path thus formed back to the battery: this is known as a short-circuit. Hopefully a short-circuit will blow a fuse, but otherwise it may cause burning of the insulation (and possibly further short-circuits) or even a fire. This is why it is inadvisable to bypass persistently blowing fuses with silver foil or wire.

Spares and tool kit

Most vehicles are supplied only with sufficient tools for wheel changing; the *Maintenance and minor repair* tool kit detailed in *Tools and working facilities,* with the addition of a hammer, is probably sufficient for those repairs that most motorists would consider attempting at the roadside. In addition a few items which can be fitted without too much trouble in the event of a breakdown should be carried. Experience and available space will modify the list below, but the following may save having to call on professional assistance:

Drivebelt(s) – emergency type may suffice
Spare fuses
Set of principal light bulbs
Tin of radiator sealer and hose bandage
Exhaust bandage
Roll of insulating tape
Length of soft iron wire
Length of electrical flex
Torch or inspection lamp (can double as test lamp)
Battery jump leads
Tow-rope
Litre of engine oil
Sealed can of hydraulic fluid
Emergency windscreen
Worm drive clips

If spare fuel is carried, a can designed for the purpose should be used to minimise risks of leakage and collision damage. A first aid kit and a warning triangle, whilst not at present compulsory in the UK, are obviously sensible items to carry in addition to the above.

When touring abroad it may be advisable to carry additional spares which, even if you cannot fit them yourself, could save having to wait while parts are obtained. The items below may be worth considering:

Clutch and throttle cables
Cylinder head gasket
Alternator brushes
Tyre valve core

One of the motoring organisations will be able to advise on availability of fuel etc in foreign countries.

Engine will not start

Engine fails to turn when starter operated
Flat battery (recharge, use jump leads, or push start)
Battery terminals loose or corroded
Battery earth to body defective
Engine earth strap loose or broken
Starter motor (or solenoid) wiring loose or broken
Starter switch faulty
Major mechanical failure (seizure)
Starter or solenoid internal fault (see Chapter 8)

Starter motor turns engine slowly
Partially discharged battery (recharge, use jump leads, or push start)
Battery terminals loose or corroded
Battery earth to body defective
Engine earth strap loose
Starter motor (or solenoid) wiring loose
Starter motor internal fault (see Chapter 8)

Starter motor spins without turning engine
Flat battery
Starter motor pinion sticking on sleeve
Flywheel gear teeth damaged or worn
Starter motor mounting bolts loose

Engine turns normally but fails to start
No fuel in tank (check for delivery at fuel filter)
Other fuel system fault (see Chapter 3)
Poor compression (see Chapter 1)
Major mechanical failure (eg camshaft drive)

Engine fires but will not run
Insufficient choke (cold engine)
Air leaks at injectors or inlet manifold
Fuel starvation (see Chapter 3)

Engine cuts out and will not restart

Fuel tank empty!
Fuel filter blocked
Fuel tank vent blocked (suction evident on removal of cap)
Other fuel system fault)
Serious overheating
Mechanical failure

Engine overheats

'Alternator' (no-charge) warning light illuminated
Slack or broken drivebelt – retension or renew (Chapter 8)

'Alternator' warning light not illuminated
Coolant loss due to internal or external leakage (see Chapter 2)
Thermostat defective
Low oil level
Brakes binding
Radiator clogged externally or internally
Cooling fan not operating correctly
Engine waterways clogged
Mixture too weak
Note: *Do not add cold water to an overheated engine or damage may result*

Low engine oil pressure

Gauge reads low or warning light illuminated with engine running
Oil level low or incorrect grade
Defective gauge or sender unit
Wire to sender unit earthed
Engine overheating
Oil filter clogged or bypass valve defective

Oil pressure relief valve defective
Oil pick-up strainer clogged
Oil pump worn or mountings loose
Worn main or big-end bearings

Note: *Low oil pressure in a high-mileage engine at tickover is not necessarily a cause for concern. Sudden pressure loss at speed is far more significant. In any event, check the gauge or warning light sender before condemning the engine.*

Engine noises

Whistling or wheezing noises

Leaking vacuum hose
Leaking manifold gasket
Blowing head gasket

Tapping or rattling

Incorrect valve clearances
Worn valve gear
Worn timing chain or gears
Broken piston ring (ticking noise)

Knocking or thumping

Unintentional mechanical contact (eg fan blades)
Worn drivebelt
Peripheral component fault (generator, water pump etc)
Worn big-end bearings (regular heavy knocking, perhaps less under load)
Worn main bearings (rumbling and knocking, perhaps worsening under load)
Piston slap (most noticeable when cold)

Excessive smoke from exhaust

Black smoke – Dirty or blocked air filter
White smoke – Unburnt fuel causing faulty combustion (at low speeds)
Blue smoke – Unburnt fuel condensing and/or worn engine

Chapter 1 Engine

Contents

Specifications

General

Type	Four-cylinder, in-line, four-stroke, overhead valve compression ignition
Engine type/code number:	
2.1 litre	XD4-90 WTA
2.3 litre	XD2/YTT (early engines) or XD2/YTR (late engines)
2.5 litre (normally aspirated)	XD3P/STP (early engines) or XD3P/STR (late engines)
2.5 litre (Turbo)	SFA
Bore and stroke:	
2.1 litre	90 x 83 mm (3.54 x 3.27 in)
2.3 litre	94 x 83 mm (3.70 x 3.27 in)
2.5 litre	94 x 90 mm (3.70 x 3.54 in)
Capacity:	
2.1 litre	2112 cc
2.3 litre	2304 cc
2.5 litre	2498 cc
Compression ratio:	
2.1 litre	22.8:1
2.3 litre	22.2:1
2.5 litre (normally aspirated)	23.0:1
2.5 litre (Turbo)	21.0:1

Firing order	1 – 3 – 4 – 2
Number 1 cylinder position	At flywheel end
Compression pressure (at cranking speed)	20 to 25 bar (290 to 360 lbf/in²)
Maximum torque (DIN):	
2.1 litre	122 Nm (90 lbf ft) at 2000 rpm
2.3 litre	139 Nm (103 lbf ft) at 2000 rpm
2.5 litre (normally aspirated)	148 Nm (108 lbf ft) at 2000 rpm
2.5 litre (Turbo)	201 Nm (148 lbf ft) at 2250 rpm
Maximum power (DIN):	
2.1 litre	46 kW (60 bhp) at 4500 rpm
2.3 litre	49 kW (64 bhp) at 4200 rpm
2.5 litre (normally aspirated)	51 kW (66 bhp) at 4200 rpm
2.5 litre (Turbo)	66 kW (88 bhp) at 4150 rpm

2.1 litre engine
Cylinder block

Cylinder block type	Cast iron. Renewable piston and liner sets
Cylinder liner flange bore	106.50 to 106.58 mm (4.1961 to 4.1992 in)
Upper liner guide bore	102.50 to 102.53 mm (4.03850 to 4.0397 in)
Lower liner seating bore	102.20 to 102.42 mm (4.0267 to 4.0353 in)
Cylinder liner bore:	
A (One stroke on liner skirt)	90.00 to 90.02 mm (3.5460 to 3.5467 in)
B (Two strokes on liner skirt)	90.02 to 90.04 mm (3.5467 to 3.5475 in)
Liner protrusion on block face	0.025 to 0.085 mm (0.0010 to 0.0033 in)
Spacer plate protrusions from sump face	0.05 to 0.15 mm (0.0020 to 0.0060 in)

Crankshaft

Main bearing journal diameter	54.994 to 55.021 mm (2.1667 to 2.1678 in)
Main bearing journal undersizes	0.30, 0.50 and 0.80 mm (0.0118, 0.0197 and 0.0315 in)
Main bearing clearance	0.040 to 0.098 mm (0.0016 to 0.0039 in)
Thrustwasher thicknesses:	
Standard	2.30 to 2.33 mm (0.0906 to 0.0918 in)
Oversize	2.50 to 2.53 mm (0.0985 to 0.0996 in)
Crankshaft endfloat	0.08 to 0.29 mm (0.0032 to 0.0114 in)
Big-end diameter	49.948 to 50.011 mm (1.968 to 1.970 in)
Big-end bearing journal undersizes	0.30, 0.50 and 0.80 mm (0.0118, 0.0197 and 0.0315 in)
Big-end bearing clearance	0.040 to 0.092 mm (0.0016 to 0.0036 in)
Big-end endfloat	0.10 to 0.25 mm (0.0039 to 0.0099 in)

Connecting rods and pistons

Small-end bush inside diameter	28.007 to 28.020 mm (1.1035 to 1.1039 in)
Small-end bush to gudgeon pin clearance	0.007 to 0.026 mm (0.0003 to 0.0010 in)
Gudgeon pin diameter:	
White	27.997 to 28.000 mm (1.1030 to 1.1032 in)
Black	27.994 to 27.997 mm (1.1029 to 1.030 in)
Gudgeon pin-to-piston clearance (at 20°C)	0.003 to 0.009 mm (0.0001 to 0.0003 in)
Piston diameter (measured under and parallel with the gudgeon pin):	
Grade A	89.900 to 89.915 mm (3.5420 to 3.5426 in)
Grade B	89.915 to 89.930 mm (3.5426 to 3.5432 in)
Piston-to-bore clearance	0.085 to 0.130 mm (0.0034 to 0.0051 in)
Piston rings:	
Top	Chromed, barrelled
Second	Cylindrical, conical
Oil scraper ring	U-flex
Piston ring gaps:	
Top	0.38 to 0.63 mm (0.0150 to 0.0248 in)
Second	0.38 to 0.60 mm (0.0150 to 0.0236 in)
Oil scraper ring	Variable (flexible)

Cylinder head

Maximum warp (diagonal)	0.2 mm (0.0078 in)
Maximum allowable regrind	0.5 mm (0.0197 in)
Valve seat angle (inlet and exhaust)	45°

Valve clearances (cold)

Inlet	0.15 to 0.20 mm (0.006 to 0.008 in)
Exhaust	0.25 to 0.30 mm (0.010 to 0.012 in)

Valve timing

Inlet opens	12° BTDC
Inlet closes	40° ABDC
Exhaust opens	56° BBDC
Exhaust closes	12° ATDC

Valves, springs and rockers

Valve head seat angle (inlet)	44° 45′ to 45°
Valve head seat depth (inlet and exhaust)	0.75 to 1.15 mm
Valve stem clearance (exhaust)	0.025 to 0.069 mm (0.0010 to 0.0027 in)
Valve stem diameter:	
Inlet	8.473 to 8.520 mm (0.3338 to 0.3357 in)
Exhaust	8.453 to 8.500 mm (0.3330 to 0.3349 in)
Valve lift (inlet and exhaust)	6.173 mm (0.2432 in)
Valve spring free length:	
Inner	41.0 mm (1.615 in)
Outer	44.6 mm (1.757 in)
Rocker shaft diameter	18.96 to 19.00 mm (0.7470 to 0.7486 in)

Camshaft

Number of bearings	Three
Bearing journal diameter	41.925 to 41.950 mm (1.6518 to 1.6528 in)
Camshaft endfloat	0.05 to 0.15 mm (0.0020 to 0.0060 in)

Timing intermediate gear endfloat

0.05 to 0.35 mm (0.0020 to 0.0138 in)

Lubrication system

Oil pump type	Rotor gears
Oil pump drive	Helical drive from camshaft
Oil pressure (hot):	
At idle speed	1.5 bar (21 lbf/in²)
At 2000 rpm	2.6 to 3.6 bar (36 to 50 lbf/in²)
Oil type/specification	Multigrade engine oil, viscosity range SAE 10W/30 to 20W/50, to API SG/CD or better (Duckhams Van Guard, QXR, or Hypergrade)
Oil filter	Champion G103
Oil capacity:	
With filter change	5.6 litres (9.9 pints)
Less filter change	5.0 litres (8.8 pints)

2.3 and 2.5 litre engines
Specifications as for 2.1 litre engine apart from the following

Cylinder block

Cylinder block type	Cast iron
Cylinder bore diameter (2.3 litre):	
Standard:	
Class A	94.000 to 94.015 mm (3.7036 to 3.7042 in)
Class B	94.015 to 94.030 mm (3.7042 to 3.7048 in)
First rebore size:	
Class C	94.200 to 94.215 mm (3.7115 to 3.7120 in)
Class D	94.215 to 94.230 mm (3.7120 to 3.7127 in)
Second rebore size:	
Class E	94.400 to 94.415 mm (3.7194 to 3.7199 in)
Class F	94.415 to 94.430 mm (3.7199 to 3.7205 in)
Third rebore size:	
Class G	94.600 to 94.615 mm (3.7272 to 3.7278 in)
Class H	94.615 to 94.630 mm (3.7278 to 3.7284 in)
Cylinder bore diameter (2.5 litre):	
Standard sizes	As per 2.3 litre, Class A or B
1st rebore size	As per 2.3 litre, Class E
2nd rebore size	94.815 to 94.830 mm (3.7357 to 3.7363 in)
Tappet bore diameter	24.00 to 24.23 mm (0.9456 to 0.9574 in)
Standard	23.95 to 23.96 mm (0.9436 to 0.9440 in)
Oversize	24.15 to 24.16 mm (0.9515 to 0.9519 in)
Tappet clearance	0.04 to 0.08 mm (0.0016 to 0.0032 in)

Crankshaft

Main bearing journal diameter:	
Standard	59.994 to 60.021 mm (2.3638 to 2.3648 in)
Undersize	0.30, 0.50 and 0.80 mm (0.0118, 0.0197 and 0.0315 in)
Main bearing clearance	0.040 to 0.098 mm (0.0016 to 0.0039 in)
Thrustwasher thicknesses:	
Standard	2.30 to 2.33 mm (0.0906 to 0.0918 in)
Oversize	2.50 to 2.53 mm (0.0985 to 0.0996 in)
Crankshaft endfloat	0.08 to 0.29 mm (0.032 to 0.0114 in)
Big-end journal diameter (2.3 litre):	
Standard	54.984 to 55.011 mm (2.1664 to 2.1674 in)
Undersize (0.30 mm, 0.0118 in)	54.684 to 54.711 mm (2.1545 to 21.556 in)
Big-end journal diameter (2.5 litre):	
Standard	54.994 to 55.021 mm (2.1668 to 2.1678 in)
Undersize (0.30 mm, 0.0118 in)	54.694 to 54.721 mm (2.1549 to 2.1560 in)

Connecting rods and pistons

Big-end bearing clearance	0.040 to 0.092 mm (0.0016 to 0.0036 in)
Big-end bearing endfloat	0.10 to 0.25 mm (0.0039 to 0.0099 in)
Small-end bush inside diameter	30.007 to 30.020 mm (1.1823 to 1.1828 in)

Piston diameter (2.3 litre – measured underneath and parallel with the gudgeon pin bore):

Standard:	
Class A	93.855 to 93.870 mm (3.6979 to 3.6985 in)
Class B	93.870 to 93.885 mm (3.6985 to 3.6991 in)
First oversize:	
Class C	94.055 to 94.070 mm (3.7058 to 3.7064 in)
Class D	94.070 to 94.085 mm (3.7064 to 3.7069 in)
Second oversize:	
Class E	94.255 to 94.270 mm (3.7136 to 3.7142 in)
Class F	94.270 to 94.285 mm (3.7142 to 3.7148 in)
Third oversize:	
Class G	94.455 to 94.470 mm (3.7215 to 3.7221 in)
Class H	94.470 to 94.485 mm (3.7221 to 3.7227 in)

Piston diameter (2.5 litre – measured at point 15.8 mm up from the base of the piston, at right-angles to the gudgeon pin bore):

Standard:	
Class A	93.855 to 93.900 mm (3.6979 to 3.6997 in)
Class B	93.900 to 93.915 mm (3.6997 to 3.7003 in)
1st Oversize	94.285 to 94.300 mm (3.7148 to 3.7154 in)
2nd Oversize	94.685 to 94.700 mm (3.7306 to 3.7312 in)

Piston protrusion at TDC:	
2.3 litre	0.54 to 0.89 mm (0.0213 to 0.0350 in)
2.5 litre:	
Normally aspirated	0.50 to 0.92 mm (0.0197 to 0.0362 in)
Turbo	0.40 to 0.87 mm (0.0158 to 0.0343 in)
Piston rings:	
Top	Chromed, spherical (trapezoidal on Turbo)
Second	Tapered (rectangular on Turbo) – TOP mark uppermost
Oil control	U-flex (TOP mark uppermost)
Piston ring gaps:	
Tap:	
Normally aspirated models	0.40 to 0.65 mm (0.0158 to 0.0256 in)
Turbo models	0.25 to 0.50 mm (0.0099 to 0.0197 in)
Second:	
Normally aspirated models	0.35 to 0.60 mm (0.0138 to 0.0236 in)
Turbo models	0.20 to 0.40 mm (0.0079 to 0.0158 in)
Oil control:	
Normally aspirated models	0.15 to 0.30 mm (0.0059 to 0.0118 in)
Turbo models	0.15 to 0.45 mm (0.0059 to 0.0177 in)
Gudgeon pin diameter:	
2.3 and 2.5 litre (STP)	27.994 to 28.00 mm (1.1030 to 1.1032 in)
2.5 litre (STR)	29.994 to 30.00 mm (1.1818 to 1.1820 in)
2.5 litre Turbo (SFA)	32.000 mm (1.2608 in)

Cylinder head

Maximum warp (diagonal)	0.2 mm (0.0078 in)
Maximum warp (transverse)	0.1 mm (0.0039 in)
Maximum regrind	0.50 mm (0.0197 in)

Cylinder head gasket thickness – 2.3 and 2.5 litre (STP):

Early type gasket:	
Piston protrusion over 0.84 mm (0.0330 in)	1.70 mm (0.0670 in)
Piston protrusion under 0.84 mm (0.0330 in)	1.58 mm (0.0623 in)
Late type gasket (with red seal band):	
Piston protrusion of 0.69 to 0.79 mm (0.0272 to 0.0311 in)	1.53 mm (0.0603 in) – two notch marks
Piston protrusion of 0.79 to 0.89 mm (0.0311 to 0.0350 in)	1.63 mm (0.0642 in) – three notch marks
Piston protrusion over 0.89 mm (0.0350 in)	1.73 mm (0.0682 in) – four notch marks

Cylinder head gasket thickness – 2.5 litre (STR and SFA):

Early type gasket:	
Piston protrusion over 0.84 mm (0.0330 in)	1.63 mm (0.0642 in)
Protrusion under 0.84 mm (0.0330 in)	1.53 mm (0.0603 in)
Late type gasket (with red seal band)	Details as per 2.3 litre late type gasket
Valve seat angle:	
2.3 litre:	
Inlet	Inlet 30°
Exhaust	Exhaust 45°
Valve seat width	2.2 to 2.5 mm (0.0867 to 0.0985 in)

Valve clearances (engine cold)

2.3 litre:	
Inlet	0.30 mm (0.012 in)
Exhaust	0.35 mm (0.014 in)

Valve clearances (engine cold) – continued

2.5 litre (naturally aspirated):

Inlet and exhaust.. 0.30 to 0.35 mm (0.012 to 0.014 in)

2.5 litre (Turbo):

Inlet.. 0.10 to 0.20 mm (0.004 to 0.008 in)

Exhaust.. 0.20 to 0.30 mm (0.008 to 0.012 in)

Valve timing

	2.3 litre	2.5 litre
Inlet opens..	12° BTDC	8° BTDC
Inlet closes..	40° ABDC	40° ABDC
Exhaust opens...	56° BBDC	56° BBDC
Exhaust closes...	12° ATDC	12° ATDC

Valves, springs and rockers

Valve head seat depth:

  2.3 litre (inlet and exhaust)... 0.75 to 1.15 mm (0.0296 to 0.0453 in)

  2.5 litre (naturally aspirated):

    Inlet .... 0.85 to 1.25 mm (0.0335 to 0.0493 in)

    Exhaust .... 1.05 to 1.45 mm (0.0414 to 0.0571 in)

  2.5 litre (Turbo):

    Inlet .... 1.05 to 1.25 mm (0.0414 to 0.0493 in)

    Exhaust .... 0.85 to 1.25 mm (0.0335 to 0.0493 in)

Valve stem-to-guide clearance (maximum)........................... 0.15 mm (0.0059 in)

Valve stem diameter:

  Inlet.. 8.473 to 8.495 mm (0.3338 to 0.3347 in)

  Exhaust... 8.453 to 8.475 mm (0.3330 to 0.3339 in)

Valve length (inlet and exhaust)... 116.25 mm (4.5802 in)

Valve lift:

  2.3 litre (inlet and exhaust):

    Early engines... 6.173 mm (0.2432 in)

    Late engines... 8.22 mm (0.3239 in)

  2.5 litre (naturally aspirated):

    Inlet .... 8.95 mm (0.3526 in)

    Exhaust .... 8.22 mm (0.3239 in)

  2.5 litre (Turbo):

    Inlet .... 8.48 mm (0.3341 in)

    Exhaust .... 8.27 mm (0.3258 mm)

Valve spring free length:

  Inner spring.. 41.0 mm (1.6154 in)

  Outer spring .... 44.6 mm (1.7572 in)

Rocker shaft diameter .... 18.96 to 19.00 mm (0.7470 to 0.7486 in)

Rocker shaft endfloat .... 0.1 mm (0.0039 in)

Camshaft

Number of bearings .... Three

Bearing journal diameter .... 41.925 to 41.950 mm (1.6518 to 1.6528 in)

Camshaft endfloat.. 0.05 to 0.15 mm (0.0020 to 0.0059 in)

Lubrication

System type... Pressurized, with a gear pump and full-flow oil filter

Minimum oil pressure at oil temperature of 80°C:

  At 650 rpm (Turbo – 875 rpm)...................................... 1.2 bar (17.4 lbf/in^2)

  At 3000 rpm .... 3.0 bar (43.5 lbf/in^2)

Oil filter (Turbo) .... Champion F108

Torque wrench settings (all engines)

	Nm	lbf ft
Cylinder head bolts:		
2.1 litre:		
Stage 1	45	33
Stage 2	70	52
Stage 3	Loosen each bolt 90°, then retighten to 70 Nm (52 lbf ft)	
Stage 4 – after 50 km (30 miles)...........................	Repeat Stage 3 operation twice	
Stage 5 – after 1200 km (750 miles).....................	Retighten bolts as per Stage 3	
2.3 and 2.5 litre:		
Stage 1	30	22
Stage 2	70	52
Stage 3 (loosen 90° and retighten)	70	52
Stage 4 (after 10 minutes at 3000 rpm then cooled for four hours):		
Early type bolts (33 mm long thread) – Tighten twice (loosen 90° and retighten)................	80	59
Late type bolts with 70 mm (2.3 litre) or 95 mm (2.5 litre) long thread – loosen 90° and retighten...................................	70	52
Stage 5 (late type bolts only)	Further tighten through 120°	

Torque wrench settings (all engines) – continued

Valve adjuster locknut	12.5 to 17.5	9.2 to 12.9
Rocker cover nuts:		
All early engines	1.5 to 3.0	1.1 to 2.2
Late 2.3 and 2.5 litre	3.0 to 4.0	2.2 to 2.9
Rocker shaft oil feed central connector	5.0 to 7.5	3.7 to 5.5
Rocker shaft studs	7.5 to 10	5.5 to 7.4
Inner rocker pedestal nuts	40 to 50	30 to 37
Outer rocker pedestal nuts	17.5 to 22.5	13 to 16.6
Pushrod tappet cover bolts	5.0 to 7.5	3.7 to 5.5
Oil feed to rocker shaft retaining bolt	15 to 20	11 to 15
Oil drain plug	25 to 35	19 to 26
Sump retaining bolts	7.5 to 12.5	5.5 to 9.2
Oil pump suction pipe bolts	5.0 to 7.5	3.7 to 5.5
Oil dipstick tube	20 to 30	15 to 22
Main oil filter retaining bolt	20 to 25	15 to 19
Timing cover and interface plate retaining bolts	7.5 to 12.5	5.5 to 9.2
Main bearing caps	100 to 120	74 to 89
Connecting rod cap nuts	53 to 62	39 to 45
Camshaft thrust/retainer plate bolts (2.1 litre)	15 to 20	11 to 15
Flywheel:		
2.1 and early 2.3 and 2.5 litre	75 to 80	55 to 59
2.3 and 2.5 litre (later models):		
Stage 1	15	11
Stage 2	95	70
Oil nozzle bolts (Turbo model)	5.0 to 7.5	3.7 to 5.5
Crankshaft pulley:		
2.1 litre:		
Original engines with 38 mm nut	220 to 240	160 to 175
Interim engines with 35 mm nut	200 to 220	150 to 160
Later engines with 22 mm bolt	220 to 240	160 to 175
2.3 and 2.5 litre	240 to 260	175 to 192
Oil pump bolts	20 to 25	15 to 19
Oil pump cap nuts	30 to 50	22 to 37
Oil pump plug	80 to 100	59 to 74
Oil pump cover bolts	5.0 to 7.5	3.7 to 5.5
Engine removal bracket bolts	10 to 12	7.4 to 8.8
Cylinder block drain plug	20 to 30	15 to 22
Engine-to-transmission bolts:		
N type transmission	40 to 50	30 to 37
MT 75 transmission	70 to 90	52 to 66
Engine mounting-to-crossmember bolts	50 to 70	30 to 52
Crossmember-to-side member bolts	70 to 90	52 to 66

1   General description

The Ford models covered by this manual may be fitted with a 2.1, 2.3 or 2.5 litre engine. All are of four-cylinder, in-line configuration, with pushrod-operated overhead valves.

The cylinder block is of cast iron on all engines. On the 2.3 and 2.5 litre engines, the cylinder bores are machined direct in the block whilst the 2.1 litre differs in using renewable wet liners.

The crankshaft is supported in the cylinder block by five renewable shell type main bearings, and crankshaft endfloat is controlled by bi-metal thrustwashers fitted to the centre main bearing. A statically and dynamically balanced flywheel is secured to the rear of the crankshaft by six bolts.

Forged steel connecting rods are used, having renewable shell type big-end bearings and bronze small-end bushes. The pistons are of aluminium alloy, each having four rings: three compression and one oil control ring.

The camshaft is of cast iron and is mounted laterally in the cylinder block. The camshaft is supported by three bearings, and is driven by helically cut spur gears from the crankshaft in the case of the 2.1 litre engine, and by a double link chain on the 2.3 and 2.5 litre engines.

An aluminium alloy cylinder head incorporating 'Ricardo Comet V' swirl chambers is fitted to all engines. The valves are retained in the cylinder head by double springs and split collets, and are operated by rocker arms via pushrods and cam followers from the camshaft.

Lubrication is by a pressure fed oil system incorporating a camshaft-driven, gear type oil pump and full-flow canister type oil filter.

Turbo engine

A 2.5 litre Turbo engine is also fitted and is similar to the 2.5 litre normally aspirated engine version except for the following items:

Oil pump – uprated type used
Cylinder head – no valve seats are used
Camshaft head – modified, but gives the same valve timing
Timing cover – has integral fan belt pulley
Oil splash nozzles – an oil splash nozzle is located at the base of each cylinder bore within the crankcase, the function of which is to cool the base of the pistons

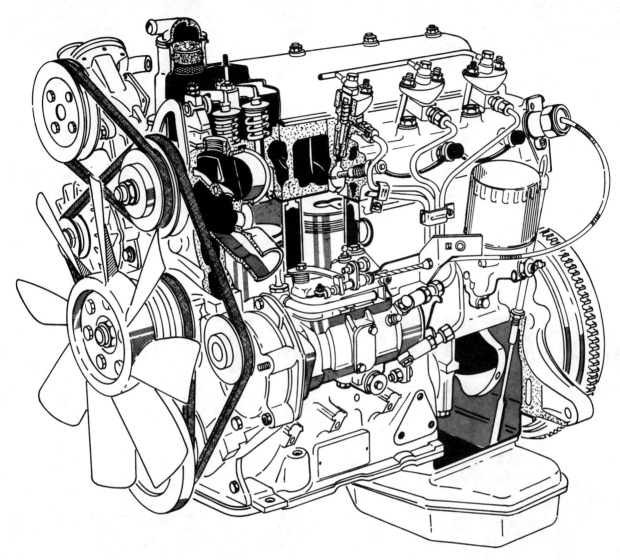

Fig. 1.1 Cut-away view of the 2.1 litre engine (Sec 1)

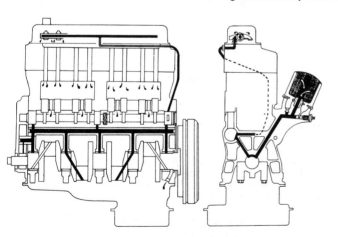

Fig. 1.2 Engine lubrication circuit (Sec 1)

2 Routine maintenance

Carry out the following procedures at the intervals given in the *'Routine maintenance'* Section at the start of this manual.

Check the engine oil level

1 The car must be parked on level ground and the engine must have been stopped for approximately 10 minutes to allow the oil in circulation to return to the sump.

2 Withdraw the dipstick from its tube, wipe clean the end of the dipstick with a piece of clean rag, re-insert it, then withdraw it again. The level of the oil on the dipstick must be between the Maximum and Minimum oil level marking cut-outs (photo).

3 It is not strictly necessary to top up the engine oil level until it has dropped to the minimum level mark, but on no account allow it to fall any lower. The amount of oil needed to top up the level from the minimum level to the maximum level is approximately 1.0 litre (1.8 pints).

4 When topping-up is necessary, use clean engine oil of the specified type. Top up by removing the filler cap from the top of the rocker cover (photo). Allow time for the oil to run down to the sump before rechecking the level of oil on the dipstick. Refit the filler cap and the dipstick on completion and wipe clean any oil which may have been accidentally spilt during topping- up.

5 It should be noted that most engines consume some oil, depending on the degree of wear and the pattern of use. Oil which is not being lost

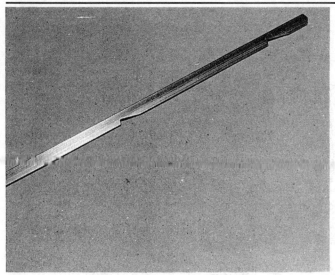

2.2 Engine oil dipstick showing Maximum and Minimum oil level cut-outs

2.4 Topping-up the engine oil level

2.7 Engine sump drain plug

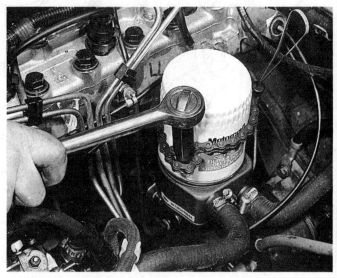

2.10A Oil filter removal using a chain wrench (2.3 litre engine)

by external leaks is lost by entering the cylinders and being burnt, although the Diesel engine is not so prone to this problem as the petrol engine since there is no inlet vacuum to suck oil past the piston rings and valves.

Renew the engine oil and oil filter

6   The engine oil should ideally be drained when it is hot (ie just after a run), with the vehicle parked on level ground and raised on axle stands at the front and rear (to keep it level). Detach and remove the engine undertray (where fitted).

7   Position a drain pan of suitable capacity under the sump drain plug and wipe the plug and surrounding area clean. Unscrew the drain plug from the sump using a hexagon key – if the oil is very hot, take care to avoid scalding (photo).

8   Remove the engine oil filler cap and allow the oil to drain for at least 15 minutes. When disposing of the used engine oil, **do not** pour it down the drain – this is illegal and causes pollution. Your dealer or Local Authority may be able to dispose of it safely.

9   Check, and if necessary renew, the drain plug washer, then wipe

clean the area around the drain hole and refit the sump drain plug. Tighten it to the specified torque.

10   The oil filter is of the disposable canister type and is removed by simply unscrewing it from the filter housing. If the filter is tight use a strap wrench or filter removing tool obtainable from most accessory shops (photos).

11   Allow for oil spillage as the filter is removed. Position rags or a suitable container under the filter mounting in which to catch the spilled oil. When the filter is removed, clean the filter mounting and the filter seal face of the mounting of old oil.

12   To fit the new filter, first smear a trace of clean engine oil around the rubber sealing ring at the base of the filter.

13   Screw the filter onto the filter housing and tighten it firmly by hand only. Do not use any tools to tighten the filter further.

14   With the new oil filter fitted, refill the engine with the correct grade and quantity of oil as previously described, but take care not to overfill.

15   Start the engine and allow it to idle. Check that the oil pressure

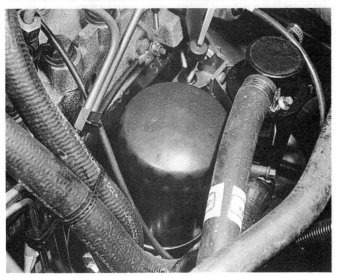

2.10B Oil filter (Turbo engine)

warning light goes out and also check that there is no oil leakage from the filter.

16   Switch off the engine and then recheck the oil level.

Clean the oil filler cap (where applicable)

17   Pull free the oil filler cap from the filler neck in the rocker cover then loosen the retaining clip and detach the crankcase ventilation hose from the cap.

18   Clean the wire mesh filter in paraffin and allow it to dry. If it is blocked with sludge, the cap must be renewed.

19   Reconnect the ventilation hose to the cap and refit the cap.

Crankcase ventilation hoses

20   Periodically inspect the crankcase ventilation hoses. Clean the hoses if they are blocked with sludge. Renew the hoses if they are cracked or broken and their retaining clips if these are in poor condition.

5.2A Disconnecting the oil pressure switch lead (2.3 litre engine)

3   Major operations possible with engine in car

The following major operations can be carried out with the engine in place in the car. It is recommended, however, that for reasons of cleanliness and accessibility the operations shown with an asterisk are performed with the engine removed.

(a)   Removal and refitting of the cylinder head and related components
(b)   Removal and refitting of the timing cover and timing components
(c)   Removal and refitting of the engine mountings
(d)   Removal and refitting of the flywheel (gearbox removed)
(e)   Removal and refitting of the sump*
(f)   Removal and refitting of the big-end bearings*
(g)   Removal and refitting of the piston and connecting rod assemblies (cylinder head removed)*
(h)   Removal and refitting of the oil pump*

4   Major operations requiring engine removal

The following operations can only be carried out satisfactorily with the engine removed from the car:

(a)   Removal and refitting of the camshaft
(b)   Removal and refitting of the crankshaft and main bearings
(c)   Removal and refitting of the cylinder liners (2.1 litre) or reboring the cylinder block (2.3 and 2.5 litre engines)

5   Oil filter mounting – removal and refitting

1   The oil filter mounting can be removed together with or without the filter but the latter is preferable since it allows greater access to the mounting fittings, and the filter element is normally easier to remove from the housing when in situ.

2   To remove the filter mounting, first disconnect the oil pressure switch lead (photos).

3   Where the filter mounting incorporates a water-cooled oil cooler, clamp the coolant hoses each side of the mounting, then detach each hose from the mounting connection (photo).

4   Place a container underneath the engine to allow for any oil spillage. Disconnect the rigid oil line, and on Turbo models the rubber oil hose, at

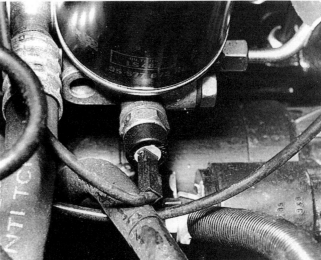

5.2B Oil pressure switch and lead (Turbo engine)

5.3 Oil cooler pipes (2.3 litre engine)

5.4 Oil pipe connection to filter housing

5.7 Locate a new gasket ...

5.8 ... and refit the filter housing (2.3 litre engine)

the mounting (photo). The rigid oil pipe supplies oil to the brake vacuum pump or the Turbo unit as applicable.

5   Undo the three retaining bolts and remove the filter mounting/oil cooler unit from the cylinder block.

6   Before refitting, ensure that the mating faces of the filter mounting and cylinder block are clean and free of oil.

7   Apply a bead of jointing compound to each side of the new gasket and position it on the filter mounting (photo).

8   Refit the filter mounting and tighten the retaining bolts (photo).

9   Where a water-cooled oil cooler is incorporated into the filter mounting, reconnect the coolant hoses to it.

10   On Turbo models, reconnect the oil cooler return hose and the oil pipe (to the turbocharger unit).

11   Reconnect the oil pressure lead to the switch unit.

12   Check and top up the engine oil level as necessary.

13   When the engine is restarted, check around the filter and its mounting connections for any sign of oil or coolant leaks.

6   **Timing cover – removal and refitting (engine in car)**

1   Disconnect the battery earth (negative) lead.

2   Detach and remove the engine undershield and, where fitted, the front insulator panels (photo).

3   Drain the cooling system and remove the radiator as described in Chapter 2 (photo).

4   Refer to Chapter 2 for details and remove the following, according to engine type:

(a)   Cooling fan drivebelt, drivebelt pulley and viscous coupling unit
(b)   Cooling fan and electro-magnetic unit
(c)   Cooling fan/power steering (PAS) pump drivebelt (Turbo models)

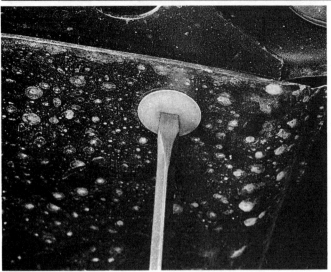

6.2 Releasing the engine undershield retaining clips

6.3 Radiator drain plug (Turbo model shown)

6.11 Timing cover oil seal renewal

6.12 Fan bearing and circlip in the timing cover

5 Refer to Section 8 in Chapter 2 and remove the other drivebelts, according to model.

6 Refer to the appropriate Chapter and remove or detach the following items from the timing cover (according to model):

(a) The alternator unit (Chapter 8)
(b) The brake vacuum unit (Chapter 5)
(c) The PAS pump unit (Chapter 7)

7 Unbolt and remove the crankshaft pulley. Recover the pulley Woodruff key. The pulley retaining nut is very tight and the crankshaft will need to be locked to prevent it from turning as the bolt is loosened off. To do this, place the car in gear and check that the handbrake is firmly applied. Alternatively, remove the starter motor (Chapter 8) and jam the flywheel ring gear with a suitable implement.

8 Extract the retaining clip and withdraw the cooling fan earth lead and brush from the holder in the top of the timing case.

9 Unscrew the retaining bolts and remove the timing cover and its gasket from the front of the engine. Note the position of any ancillary items (such as the drivebelt adjuster strap/jockey wheel unit) which are

also attached by the cover bolts.

10 The removal and inspection of the timing components and their refitting details are described separately in this Chapter.

11 The timing cover oil seal can be renewed by carefully prising out the old seal, then supporting the housing on its underside and driving the new seal into the cover ensuring that the seal lip faces downwards (photo).

12 If the fan/shaft bearings are in need of renewal, extract the circlip, then heat up the timing cover in hot water (not with a naked flame). Tap the cover at the points shown in Fig. 1.3 whilst supporting the shaft and remove the bearing and shaft unit. Renew the shaft and bearing assembly complete. Press the new unit into position then fit a new circlip into the groove in the cover to secure (photo).

13 Refitting of the timing cover is a reversal of the removal procedure, but note the following special points:

(a) Ensure that the mating faces are clean and fit a new gasket but take care not to damage it as it is passed over the timing gears, or sprockets, as applicable

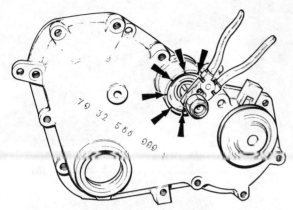

Fig. 1.3 Fan shaft and bearing removal method – tap the housing at the points indicated (Sec 6)

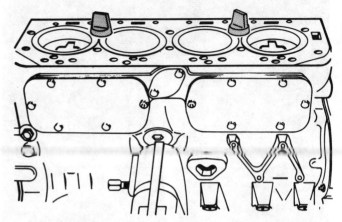

Fig. 1.4 Cylinder liner clamps – 2.1 litre engine (Sec 7)

(b)   When refitting the drivebelt pulley to the crankshaft, thoroughly clean the retaining bolt threads and treat them with thread-locking compound. Tighten the bolt to the specified torque setting

(c)   Tighten all fixings to their specified torque wrench settings, where these are given, and adjust the drivebelt tensions as described in Chapter 2

(d)   Refit the radiator and refill the cooling system as described in Chapter 2

(e)   When the engine is restarted, check for any signs of oil or coolant leaks from the timing cover and radiator coolant hose connections

---

7   Cylinder head – removal (engine in car)

Note: *The engine must have fully cooled for a minimum period of six hours before the cylinder head is removed*

1   Disconnect the battery earth (negative) lead.

2   Remove the air cleaner unit and mountings as described in Chapter 3. On Turbo models, the air cleaner unit can be left in position, but the air pipe between the cleaner and the manifold must be detached, as must the crankcase ventilation hose from the rocker cover.

3   Where applicable, detach and remove the engine undertray.

4   Drain the engine coolant as described in Chapter 2.

5   Disconnect the cooling and heater hoses from the cylinder head. Note their connections and routing (photos).

6   Disconnect the following wiring connections from the cylinder head (photos):

(a)   The main supply lead to the number 4 glow plug
(b)   Temperature sensor unit
(c)   Temperature gauge sender unit
(d)   Engine harness lead connector

7   On Turbo models, disconnect and unbolt the dipstick/crankcase ventilation filter support bracket from the cylinder head on the left-hand side (photo).

8   Detach the cold start idle speed control cable from the cylinder head as described in Chapter 3.

9   Refer to Chapter 3 and detach the fuel lines and the leak-off hoses from the injection pump. Plug the lines and hoses to prevent the ingress of dirt.

10   On Turbo models, detach the exhaust fume limited hose from the connection on top of the inlet manifold and move the hose out of the way.

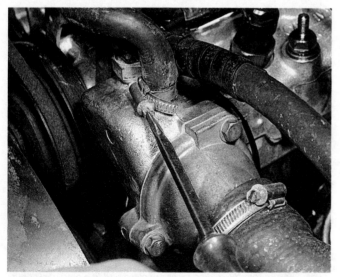

7.5A Detach the engine coolant hoses ...

7.5B ... and heater hoses

7.5C Heater hose connection on the Turbo model

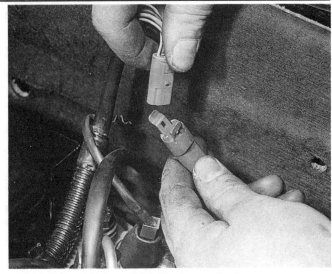

7.6A Disconnecting the engine wiring harness lead ...

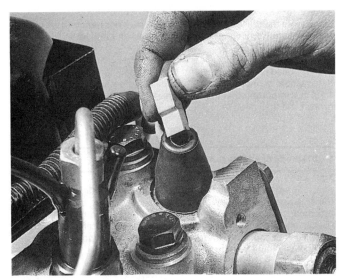

7.6B ... and temperature sensor wire

11 Unscrew the retaining bolt and detach the rocker shaft lubrication pipe from the side of the cylinder head above the manifolds. Collect the seal washers from each side of the pipe union – these washers must be renewed. Undo the screw and detach the oil pipe dual clip from the rear of the cylinder head (photo).

12 Working underneath the car, unbolt and detach the exhaust down-pipe from the manifold (photo). On Turbo models also detach the following from the turbo unit:

(a) *The oil feed and return pipes*
(b) *Unbolt and detach the oil feed pipe from the clip attached to the manifold. (This clip also secures the rocker shaft oil feed pipe)*

13 Remove the alternator, water pump and/or brake vacuum pump drivebelts as described in Chapter 2.

14 Detach and remove the following from the cylinder head:

(a) *The brake vacuum pump – see Chapter 5 (photo)*
(b) *The alternator unit (Chapter 8)*

15 Unscrew the four retaining nuts and remove the rocker cover and the hose bracket (photo), but take care not to damage the rocker cover gasket as it is removed. A silicone seal is used on later type rocker

7.7 Unclip the crankcase ventilation hose assembly

7.11 Oil feed pipe and location clip attachment on rear face of cylinder head

7.12 Exhaust downpipe to manifold joint flange (2.3 litre engine)

7.14 Oil pipe connection to the vacuum pump unit (2.3 litre engine)

7.15 Unscrew nuts and remove rocker cover (2.3 litre engine)

covers (identified in not having a lip on the mating surface), and if the seal is in good condition, it can be left in position on the cover and re-used.

16   Undo and remove the four nuts and two bolts securing the rocker shaft assembly to the cylinder head and carefully lift the rocker gear off the studs.

17   Now carefully lift out each pushrod, while at the same time twisting it to free the cam follower. Keep the pushrods in order by punching eight holes in a piece of cardboard, numbering the holes and inserting each pushrod as it is removed.

18   Undo all the cylinder head retaining bolts in a progressive manner in the reverse order to that shown in Fig. 1.17 (according to type) and then remove them from the cylinder head.

19   With all the bolts removed lift the cylinder head from the block. If the head is stuck, try to rock it to break the seal. *Under no circumstances try to prise it apart from the cylinder block using a screwdriver or cold chisel*, as damage may be caused to the mating surfaces of the cylinder head and block. If it is extremely stubborn strike the head sharply with a soft-faced mallet until it is free.

20   Carefully lift the old head gasket from the top face of the cylinder

block. Note that the gasket has thickness markings denoting which type to obtain when renewing it, so keep the gasket for reference.

21   To stop the cylinder liners moving on the 2.1 litre engine when the cylinder head is removed, clamp them in position using two bolts and flat washers screwed into the cylinder head retaining bolt holes (Fig. 1.15). It is important that the liners are not disturbed or their seals will be broken and then need renewal – see Sections 27 and 40.

8   Methods of engine removal

The engine may be lifted out either on its own or in unit with the transmission. If the engine is to be removed with the transmission still attached, considerable dismantling work must be carried out beneath the car, and in addition a very substantial crane and preferably a ramp or pit will be needed. It is therefore recommended that whenever possible the engine should be removed separately.

9   Engine and transmission – removal

1   Position the car over an inspection pit or on a ramp. If these are not available, jack up the front and rear of the car and support it on axle stands.

2   Raise and support the bonnet and with the aid of an assistant, undo the hinge bolts, lift the bonnet from the car and store it in a safe area (photo). On Turbo models unclip and remove the anti-rattle pad from the bonnet right-hand hinge and the plastic cover from the washer hose nozzle for access.

3   Remove the air cleaner unit as described in Chapter 3.

4   On Turbo models, detach and remove the air intake pipe and the crankcase ventilation hose.

5   Detach and remove the radiator upper shroud. The shroud is secured to the radiator by two clips and two screws.

6   Where applicable, detach and remove the engine undertray.

7   Position a suitable container under the radiator drain plug, loosen off the plug and drain the coolant into the container. As the bottom hose is slightly lower than the radiator, disconnect the hose and drain the remaining coolant from there. To drain the cylinder block, remove the

9.2 Removing the bonnet

9.9 Detach the engine coolant hoses

9.11 Fuel injection pump and connections (2.3 litre engine)

9.12 Disconnecting the engine stop switch wire

drain plugs from their locations in the block, on each side towards the rear.

8   Where fitted, unclip and remove the soundproofing from the front of the engine compartment.

9   Disconnect the following cooling system hoses, as applicable (photo):

   (a)   The radiator top and bottom hoses
   (b)   The coolant expansion (degas) tank hoses
   (c)   The coolant heater hoses from the cylinder head and oil cooler

10   Detach the vacuum hose from the brake vacuum pump and pull it free from the servo unit (naturally aspirated models).

11   Disconnect the fuel supply and leak-off lines from the pump unit (photo). Plug them to prevent excess leakage of fuel and the ingress of dirt.

12   Disconnect the following wires, noting their locations and routing as they are detached:

   (a)   Alternator
   (b)   Starter motor and the earth strap to starter motor retaining bolt
   (c)   Main supply lead to the rearmost glow plug
   (d)   The temperature gauge sender unit and sensor unit on the cylinder head and thermostat housing
   (e)   The oil pressure sender switch
   (f)   Engine stop switch wire from the injector pump (photo)
   (g)   Cooling fan electro-magnetic clutch
   (h)   Radiator temperature sensor

13   Remove the engine wiring loom from the engine and position it out of the way. If preferred, the loom can be separated at the in-line plug located at the rear of the cylinder head.

14   Disconnect the accelerator cable from the injector pump unit as described in Chapter 3. Move the cable out of the way.

15   Remove the radiator as described in Chapter 2.

16   On Turbo models, disconnect the fuel filter from its support bracket and move it aside. Disconnect the oil cooler lines from the base of the oil cooler/filter.

9.21 Disconnect and remove the starter motor. Note earth lead secured by top retaining bolt

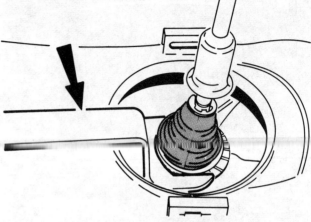

Fig. 1.5 Unscrew the gear lever ball cap with special cranked spanner (arrowed) – 2.1 litre model (Sec 9)

17   Unbolt the air cleaner support bracket from the rear of the cylinder head and in its place fit a suitable engine lift bracket (where necessary).

18   Unscrew the retaining bolts and detach the exhaust downpipe from the manifold. On Turbo models, undo the two front nuts and detach the front exhaust pipe from the turbocharger. Release the exhaust system from its underbody insulators and remove it from the vehicle as a unit.

19   Remove the drivebelt(s) from the PAS pump, water pump, brake vacuum pump and the alternator as applicable (see Chapter 2).

20   Unscrew the retaining nut and remove the cooling fan and its clutch unit.

21   Remove the starter motor as described in Chapter 8 (photo), then jam the starter ring gear on the flywheel with a suitable tool and loosen off the crankshaft pulley bolt.

22   Remove the crankshaft pulley bolt, washer and pulley. Collect the Woodruff key from the groove in the crankshaft.

23   Unbolt and remove the alternator and, where applicable, unbolt the power steering pump from its bracket and move the pump out of the way, leaving its hoses attached to it. Also unbolt and remove the water pump drivebelt adjuster.

24   On naturally aspirated models, unscrew and remove the gear lever knob. Detach the console tray or the complete console (if the short console type is fitted). Detach any wiring connections from the console.

25   Also on naturally aspirated models, unclip the gear lever gaiter and withdraw them up the lever. On 2.1 litre models, use a cranked spanner and unscrew the gear lever ball cup (Fig. 1.5). On 2.3 and 2.5 litre models, undo the retaining screws to detach the gear lever from the transmission extension housing.

26   Unbolt and remove the stabilizer (anti-roll bar).

27   Detach and withdraw the propeller shaft from the transmission. If the rear wheels are off the ground, put the handbrake on to ensure that the propeller shaft does not turn when loosening the bolts securing the propeller shaft. The procedure differs according to model.

28   On normally aspirated models, make an alignment mark across the outer face of the universal joint flange (at the transmission end) to ensure correct realignment when reassembling. Undo the four flange bolts, then supporting the shaft, unscrew the centre bearing-to-floor bolts, then lower and withdraw the shaft rearwards so that it is clear of

the transmission. Plug the end of the extension housing to prevent the loss of oil from the transmission during removal.

29   On Turbo models, make an alignment mark across the propeller shaft joint flange at the rear axle end to ensure correct realignment during reassembly. Unscrew the four flange-to-axle bolts, support the shaft and undo the centre bearing-to-floor bolts, then unscrew and remove the three flange nuts at the transmission end. Withdraw the propeller shaft. Unscrew the three torx bolts and remove the vibration damper from the transmission.

30   On 2.1 litre and normally aspirated 2.5 litre models, pull back the gaiter and detach the clutch cable from the release lever by pulling the lever back by hand and sliding the cable nipple free through the larger aperture of the slotted location hole in the lever.

31   On the 2.3 litre Sierra model, position a wooden block under the clutch pedal to raise it fully so that the automatic adjuster pawl is held clear of the toothed segment. Prise free the gaiter from the release lever, disconnect the cable and feed it through the clutch housing.

32   To detach the clutch cable on Turbo models, pull back the gaiter, remove the lock clip and damper weight, then detach the cable.

33   Position a jack (trolley type if possible) under the transmission. Raise the jack to just support the weight of the transmission.

34   Attach a lift sling to the engine lifting brackets (photos) and take the weight of the engine. When attaching the lift sling, allow for a steep angle of lift when withdrawing the engine and transmission unit.

35   Unscrew and remove the engine bearer nut from the crossmember each side.

36   Unscrew the transmission-to-crossmember bolt, also the crossmember-to-floor securing bolts. Remove the crossmember, heat shield and, where applicable, disconnect the earth strap.

37   Lower the transmission sufficiently to enable the speedometer drive cable to be detached from the transmission. Extract the retaining clip and pull the cable free.

38   On Turbo models, undo the two screws retaining the shift mechanism to the transmission, unclip the shift rod and withdraw the shift mechanism unit. Slightly raise the engine if required to allow additional access.

39   Detach the reversing light switch and, where applicable, the speed sensor lead.

40   Removal of the engine mounting (bearer) arm on each side will allow greater room for manoeuvre when withdrawing the engine and transmission from the car (photos).

9.34A Engine lifting bracket – front (Turbo model)

9.34B Engine lifting bracket – rear (Turbo model)

9.40A Remove the retaining nut ...

9.40B ... and bolts ...

9.40C ... and remove the engine mounting arms

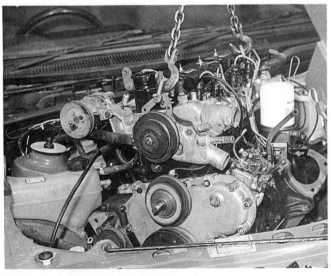

9.41 Engine removal (2.3 litre shown)

41   Check that all fittings and connections are clear of the engine and transmission. Raise the engine and transmission (photo), simultaneously pulling it forwards. As they are pulled forward, lower the transmission to allow a greater angle of lift. An assistant will be required to help guide the engine/transmission clear of the fittings in the engine compartment. If there is insufficient clearance, it will be necessary to jack the front of the car up to allow further room for manoeuvre, but ensure that the car is fully supported on axle stands before proceeding. On Turbo models take particular care not to damage the heat shields and ABS unit.

42   When the engine/transmission is clear of the engine compartment, move the car rearward of the engine/transmission forward so that it is clear of the vehicle, then lower it to the floor.

43   Before removing the lift sling support the unit with blocks so that it cannot roll over.

10   Engine only – removal

1   Proceed as described for engine and transmission removal in the previous Section paragraphs 1 to 22 inclusive then paragraphs 30 and 32. Note that the exhaust system can be left in position, but must of course be detached from the manifold/turbo unit.

2   On Turbo models, it is advisable to detach and remove the manifolds and the turbo unit from the engine in order to allow sufficient clearance for manoeuvre when lifting the engine from the vehicle. The power steering pump and the alternator should also be removed.

3   Unscrew and remove the engine-to-transmission retaining bolts.

4   Attach a lift sling to the engine so that it is supported horizontally.

5   The front crossmember under the engine will need to be lowered in order to provide the necessary sump clearance as the engine is removed. Check that the engine and transmission are suitably supported, then loosen off the crossmember-to-body retaining bolts each side and lower the crossmember about 2.5 inches. As the crossmember is lowered, ensure that the brake lines attached to it do not over-stretch and distort or fracture. If necessary, disconnect the lines to allow the crossmember to be lowered the required amount. It may also be necessary to disconnect the steering column lower coupling.

6   Raise the engine and the transmission as far as possible, the travel being limited by the latter coming into contact with the transmission tunnel. Check that the engine is clear of its mountings and that all of the associate fittings are detached and out of the way, then pull the engine from the transmission. Do not allow the weight of the engine to hang on the transmission input shaft during withdrawal from it. When clear of the input shaft, swing the engine round so that it is pointing towards the front right-hand corner of the car. The aid of an assistant is necessary during this part of the operation to help guide the engine clear of the surrounding compartment, then lower it to the ground. Support it with blocks to ensure that it does not topple over when the sling is detached.

11   Engine – separation from transmission

1   If the engine has been removed complete with the transmission, these units must be separated before engine dismantling can begin.

2   Undo and remove the bolts securing the starter motor flange to the bellhousing and the additional bolt, where fitted, securing the starter motor rear support bracket to the cylinder block. Now lift off the starter motor and closure plate.

3   Undo and remove the bolts securing the closure plate to the bellhousing and lift away the plate.

4   Undo and remove the bolt securing the bellhousing to the engine.

5   With the help of an assistant withdraw the transmission from the rear of the engine.

12   Engine – dismantling (general)

1   It is best to mount the engine on a dismantling stand, but if this is not available, then stand the engine on a strong bench so as to be at a comfortable working height.

2   During the dismantling process the greatest care should be taken to keep exposed parts free of dirt. As an aid to achieving this, it is a sound scheme to thoroughly clean down the outside of the engine, removing all traces of oil and congealed dirt.

3   Use paraffin or a good grease solvent. The latter compound will make the job easier, as, after the solvent has been applied and allowed to stand for a time, a vigorous jet of water will wash off the solvent and all the grease and filth. if the dirt is thick and deeply embedded, work the solvent into it with a stiff paint brush.

4   Finally wipe down the exterior of the engine with a rag, and only then when it is quite clean should the dismantling process begin. As the engine is stripped, clean each part in a bath of paraffin.

5   Never immerse parts with oilways in paraffin (eg the crankshaft), but to clean wipe down carefully with a paraffin moistened rag. Oilways can be cleaned out with nylon pipe cleaners. If an air line is present all parts can be blown dry and the oilways blown through as an added precaution.

6   Re-use of old engine gaskets is a false economy and can give rise to oil and water leaks, if nothing worse. To avoid the possibility of trouble after the engine has been reassembled, always use new gaskets throughout.

7   Do not throw the old gaskets away as it sometimes happens that an immediate replacement cannot be found, and the old gasket is then very useful as a template. Hang up the old gaskets as they are removed on a suitable hook or nail.

8   When purchasing engine gaskets be particularly careful to state the type of engine fitted. Also take care when obtaining a replacement cylinder head gasket or cylinder head bolts as there are three different types of each available.

9   To strip the engine it is best to work from the top down. The oil sump and suitable wood packing provides a firm base on which the engine can be supported in an upright position. When the stage where the sump must be removed is reached, the engine can be turned on its side and all other work carried out with it in this position.

10   Whenever possible, refit nuts, bolts and washers fingertight from wherever they were removed. This helps to avoid later loss and muddle. If they cannot be refitted then lay them out in such a fashion that it is clear from where they came.

11   It may be that the engine being worked on has one or more modifications that are not shown in the photographs or illustrations. Should this occur make a note of any differences.

13   Ancillary components – removal

1   With the engine removed from the car and thoroughly cleaned, the externally mounted ancillary components should now be removed before any major dismantling begins.

2   Depending on the extent of the dismantling, the following items should be removed:

   (a) *Vacuum pump (Chapter 5)*
   (b) *Cooling fan and fan hub (Chapter 2)*
   (c) *Water pump (Chapter 2)*
   (d) *Fuel injection pump (Chapter 3)*
   (e) *Fuel injectors (Chapter 3)*
   (f) *Glow plugs (Chapter 3)*
   (g) *Clutch unit (Chapter 3)*
   (h) *Oil feed pipe to rocker shaft assembly from cylinder block*
   (i) *Oil filter and housing (Section 5)*
   (j) *Inlet/exhaust manifolds and where applicable, the turbo unit (Chapter 3)*
   (k) *Engine mounting arms*

14   Cylinder head – removal (engine out of car)

The procedure for removal of the cylinder head with the engine out of the car is similar to that for removal when the engine is fitted, with the exception of disconnecting the controls and fixtures. Refer to Section 7 and follow paragraphs 15 to 21 inclusive.

15   Cylinder head – dismantling

1   Prior to dismantling the cylinder head, detach and remove items (c), (e), (f) and (j) in Section 13.

2   The valves can be removed from the cylinder head by the following method. Compress each spring in turn with a valve spring compressor until the two halves of the collet can be removed. Release the compressor and lift off the inner and outer springs, the spring cap and spring seat (Fig. 1.6).

3   If, when the valve spring compressor is screwed down, the valve spring cap refuses to free to expose the split collet, do not continue to screw down on the compressor as there is a likelihood of damaging it.

4   Gently tap the top of the tool directly over the valve spring cap with a soft-faced mallet. This will free the cap. To avoid the compressor jumping off the valve spring cap when it is tapped, hold the compressor firmly in one hand.

5   On naturally aspirated models, slide the rubber oil seals off the inlet valve stems (seals are not fitted to Turbo models).

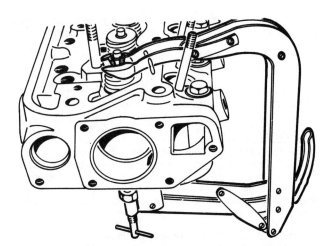

Fig. 1.6 Valve assembly removal from the cylinder head using a spring compressor (Sec 15)

6   Withdraw each valve in turn from its guide. It is essential that the valves are kept in their correct sequence unless they are so badly worn that they are to be renewed. Punch eight holes in a piece of cardboard as was done previously for the pushrods and insert the valves in their correct hole as they are removed.

16   Timing cover and timing components – removal (engine out of car)

1   Using a large socket and extension bar, undo and remove the crankshaft pulley retaining nut. To stop the crankshaft from turning as the nut is undone, use a large screwdriver engaged with the starter ring gear teeth and in contact with the cylinder block.

2   With the nut removed, ease off the pulley using two levers placed behind the pulley at opposite points to remove it. Once the pulley is off, recover the Woodruff key from the end of the crankshaft and place it somewhere safe, as it is easily lost.

3   Now undo and remove the nuts, plain and socket-headed bolts securing the timing cover to the front of the engine. Lift off the cover and recover the gasket. Note that on 2.3 and 2.5 litre models fitted with a viscous fan pulley, the pulley and cover are removed together and the two cover bolts on the underside of the pulley are not removable from the cover.

4   The removal sequence now differs according to engine.

2.1 litre engine (with gear-driven timing components)
5   Turn the engine over by means of the flywheel until the timing reference marks on the gears are all opposite each other. **Note:** *This only occurs once every 22 revolutions of the crankshaft.*

6   The fuel injection pump and its timing gear will already have been removed if the engine dismantling sequence has been closely followed. If the injection pump is still in place, refer to Chapter 3 and remove it at this stage.

7   Using circlip pliers extract the idler (intermediate) gear retaining circlip. Lift off the thrustwashers followed by the gear.

8   The crankshaft pinion gear can now be removed using two levers to ease it off the front of the crankshaft. Recover the Woodruff key and put it in a safe place.

9   Do not attempt to remove the camshaft gear as this is removed with the camshaft as described in Section 20.

2.3 and 2.5 litre engine (with chain-driven timing components)
10   Clean the front face of the timing sprockets and chain, then check that the three timing paint marks are clearly visible on the appropriate chain links. When the engine is turned to the timing position, these painted links must align with the timing reference marks on the crankshaft sprocket (set at TDC), the camshaft sprocket and the fuel injection pump sprocket.

11   Insert the blade of a small screwdriver into the access aperture in the body of the chain tensioner and turn the tensioner lock to retract and immobilize the tensioner.

12   Loosen off the chain roller sprocket bolt and engage an Allen key into the eccentric plate. Turn the plate to release the tension of the sprocket on the chain, then withdraw the chain together with the injection pump sprocket. As the chain is removed from the tensioner, ensure that the tensioner slipper is locked in position or it (and its associate components) will fly out of the tensioner body when released.

13   Unscrew the retaining nut and bolt and remove the chain tensioner unit.

14 Unscrew the roller sprocket retaining bolt and remove the sprocket.

15 Using two levers, carefully ease the crankshaft sprocket forward and off the crankshaft. Recover the Woodruff key from the shaft groove and store it in a safe place.

16 Do not attempt to remove the camshaft and sprocket at this stage.

17 Flywheel – removal

1 Where applicable, use a screwdriver or chisel and knock back the locking tabs from the flywheel retaining bolts. Lock the flywheel by jamming the starter ring gear teeth with a screwdriver or suitable tool, then unscrew and remove the flywheel retaining bolts.

2 With the bolts removed, lift off the locking plate (if fitted) and suitably mark the relationship of the flywheel to the crankshaft flange as a guide to refitment.

3 Now lift off the flywheel.

18 Sump – removal

1 If the engine is already removed from the car, proceed as described in paragraph 9.

2 If the engine is in the car, raise and support the car at the front and rear so that it is kept level. Do not position the axle stands under the front crossmember.

3 Detach and remove the engine undertray (if fitted), then undo the drain plug and drain the engine oil into a suitable container. Refit the drain plug when draining is complete.

4 On Turbo models, loosen off the clip and detach the oil return hose from the sump on the left-hand side.

5 Disconnect the battery earth (negative) lead. Remove the air cleaner unit (or air hose to the cleaner on Turbo models).

6 Where applicable, unclip the front soundproofing, then undo the two retaining bolts, release the retaining clips and remove the radiator upper shroud.

7 Fit an engine support bar or lift sling and support the weight of the engine. Unscrew and remove the engine mountings from their bearers, then raise the engine slightly.

8 Working underneath the car, progressively loosen off the bolts securing the crossmember to the body. Do not fully remove the bolts, but lower the crossmember about 2.5 inches to allow the necessary sump removal clearance. Note that the brake lines are secured to the crossmember each side and care must be taken not to damage them. If necessary, disconnect the brake lines if they are under pressure and likely to distort or fracture. The steering column lower coupling may also need to be disconnected to allow the crossmember to be lowered the required amount.

9 Unscrew the sump retaining bolts and lower the sump from the engine. If it is stuck, tap it free using a soft-headed mallet. As it is withdrawn, allow for oil spillage from the sump and the crankcase.

19 Oil pump – removal

1 Undo and remove the large socket-headed thrust plug from the right-hand side of the cylinder block, taking care not to lose any shims that may be fitted under the plug.

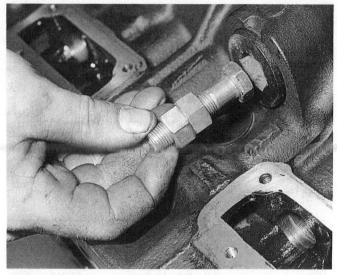

19.2 Improvised tool for removal/refitting of thrust plug

2 If a suitable 19 mm key is not available to unscrew the thrust plug, use a $\frac{1}{2}$ in UNF bolt with a $\frac{3}{4}$ in hexagonal head and two locknuts fitted to the bolt as shown to remove and subsequently to tighten the plug (photo).

3 Undo and remove the domed nut located just below the previously removed thrust plug.

4 With the domed nut removed, the oil pump retaining grub screw will be exposed. Unscrew the grub screw and then slide the oil pump out of the crankcase.

20 Camshaft and tappets – removal

1 Remove the bolts securing the tappet side covers then remove the covers and gaskets. Note the position of the oil pipe retaining clip.

2.1 litre engine

2 Extract the tappets upwards from their ports in the cylinder block and withdraw them from the side cover apertures. Keep them in their order of fitting.

3 Undo and remove the two camshaft thrust plate securing bolts which are accessible using a socket through the holes in the camshaft gear. Now carefully withdraw the camshaft from the front of the engine, taking care not to damage the camshaft bearings as the camshaft passes through them.

4 Undo and remove the remaining nuts securing the interface plate to the cylinder block and lift it off complete with gasket.

2.3 and 2.5 litre engines

5 The tappets cannot be withdrawn upwards from their ports in the cylinder block, only downwards after the camshaft has been removed. Invert the block or position it on its side with the tappet cover apertures up so that the tappets are not bearing on the camshaft. This will ease camshaft removal and prevent the tappets from falling out when the camshaft is withdrawn.

6 To remove the camshaft, undo the four interface plate retaining bolts, then withdraw the interface plate and camshaft from the engine. As they are withdrawn, disengage the plate from the camshaft and separate the two.

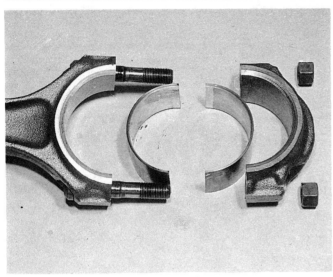

21.7 Connecting rod, bearing shells and cap

7 Extract the respective tappets from the cylinder block, keeping them in their order of fitting.

21 Pistons and connecting rods – removal

1 The pistons and connecting rods can be removed with the engine still in the car or while it is out during a major overhaul. With the 2.1 litre engine, the piston/rod assemblies can be removed together with their liners. Alternatively, if the liners are to remain in the block, they must be clamped down (see Section 7, paragraph 21) to prevent them from moving as the piston/rod assemblies are withdrawn upwards through them.

2 With the cylinder head and sump removed, undo and remove the big-end cap retaining nuts.

3 Remove the big-end caps one at a time, taking care to keep them in the right order and the correct way round. Also ensure that the shell bearings are kept with their correct connecting rods and caps unless they are to be renewed.

4 It is a good idea to mark the side face of each rod and cap with identification marks using a centre punch and light hammer (unless they are already marked). Use a single dot for No 1 connecting rod and cap, two dots from No 2, and so on. This will ensure there is no mix-up on reassembly, as it is very important that the caps are refitted to the connecting rods from which they are removed.

5 If the big-end caps are difficult to remove they may be gently tapped with a soft-faced mallet.

6 To remove the shell bearings, press the bearing opposite the groove in both the connecting rod and the connecting rod caps and the bearings will slide out easily.

7 Push the connecting rod upwards, tapping gently with a block of wood until the piston emerges from the top of the cylinder bore. Now lift the piston and connecting rod assembly out of its cylinder and keep it in the correct order for refitment in the same bore (photo).

22 Crankshaft and main bearings – removal

1 Mark the main bearing caps and cylinder block faces to ensure that the caps are refitted the correct way round and in the correct order.

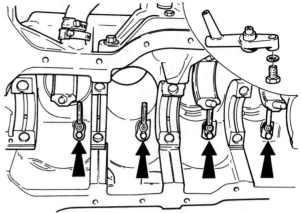

Fig. 1.7 Oil splash nozzle locations (arrowed) in the 2.5 litre Turbo engine cylinder block (Sec 22)

2 Undo and remove the bolts securing the five main bearing caps to the cylinder block.

3 Tap the caps lightly using a soft-faced mallet to free them, and then lift off each cap and the bottom half of each bearing shell. Take care to keep the bearing shells in the right caps.

4 When removing the centre bearing cap recover the two semi-circular thrustwashers from either side of the cap. Lay the thrustwashers together with the cap.

5 Now carefully lift out the crankshaft. Remove the upper halves of the main bearing shells and lay them down with their respective lower halves and bearing caps. Recover also the remaining two thrustwashers from the centre main bearing.

6 On Turbo models, the oil nozzles at the base of each cylinder bore can be removed by unscrewing the retaining bolt. Remove the bolt, seal washer and oil nozzle from each cylinder in turn (Fig. 1.7).

23 Engine components – examination for wear

When the engine has been stripped down and all parts properly cleaned, decisions have to be made as to what needs renewal, and the following Sections tell the examiner what to look for. In any borderline case it is always best to decide in favour of a new part. Even if a part may still be serviceable its life will have been reduced by wear and the degree of trouble needed to renew it in the future must be taken into consideration. However, these things are relative and it depends on whether a quick 'survival' job is being done or whether the car as a whole is being regarded as having many thousands of miles of useful and economical life remaining.

24 Oil pump – examination

1 Unscrew the retaining bolts and remove the oil pick-up pipe from the pump unit.

2 Undo the four retaining bolts and withdraw the end cover from the pump body (photo). Note that the cover is under tension from the oil pressure relief valve and spring.

3 With the cover removed, the relief valve and spring can be extracted from their location in the pump. Lift out each pump gear in turn for inspection but keep them correctly orientated for position of fitting. Withdraw the drivegear and shaft (photo).

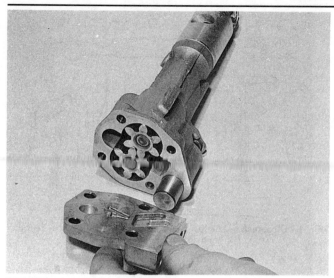

24.2 Remove the oil pump end cover ...

24.3A ... withdraw the relief valve and spring ...

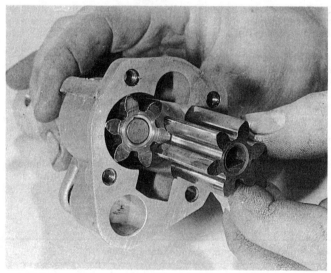

24.3B ... extract the rotors ...

24.3C ... and the driveshaft and gear

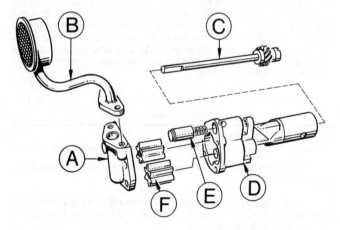

Fig. 1.8 Engine oil pump components (Sec 24)

A	Cover	D	Body
B	Oil pick-up tube	E	Relief valve
C	Drive shaft and gear	F	Rotors

4   With the pump dismantled and the parts laid out for inspection, check first the pump body for any signs of scoring or wear on the internal walls. Refit the driveshaft to the pump body and check for excessive side-to-side movement of the shaft.

5   Closely examine the teeth of the pump gears for pitting, scoring or wear ridges. Refit the gears to the pump and check for any side-to-side movement or excessive backlash of the gears.

6   Check the oil pump cover for wear ridges or grooving caused by excessive endfloat of the gears.

7   Finally, inspect the oil pressure relief valve for wear and ensure that it is free to move in its bore without sticking. Check also that the relief spring is sound with no signs of distortion or weakening of the coils.

8   If any of the oil pump components were found to be worn, scored or in any way suspect, the pump should be renewed. Generally speaking if the engine has covered a high mileage and is being reconditioned or overhauled, it is advisable to renew the pump as a matter of course.

9   If, however, the oil pump components are in a satisfactory condition, the pump should be reassembled using the reverse sequence to

removal. Thoroughly lubricate all the parts in engine oil during assembly and fill the pumping chambers around the gears with engine oil before refitting the oil pump cover and pick-up strainer assembly.

25 Crankshaft – examination and renovation

1 Examine the bearing surface of the crankshaft for scratches or scoring and, using a multimeter, check each journal and crankpin for ovality. Where this is found to be in excess of 0.0254 mm (0.001 in) the crankshaft will have to be reground and undersize bearings fitted.

2 An accurate method of determining bearing wear is by the use of Plastigage. The crankshaft is located in the main bearings (and big-end bearings if necessary) and the Plastigage filament located across the journal, which must be dry. The cap is then fitted and the bolts/nuts tightened to the specified torque. On removal of the cap the width of the filaments is checked against a scale which shows the bearing running clearance. This clearance is then compared with that given in the Specifications (photos).

3 Crankshaft regrinding should be carried out by a suitable engineering works, who will normally supply the matching undersize main and big-end shell bearings.

4 Note that undersize bearings may already have been fitted, either in production or by a previous repairer. Check the markings on the backs of the old bearing shells, and if in doubt take them along when buying new ones. Production undersizes are also indicated by paint marks on the main bearing cups or the crankshaft web, in which case your Ford parts dealer will advise your bearing requirements (photos).

5 If the crankshaft endfloat is more than the maximum specified amount, new thrustwashers should be fitted to the centre main bearings. These are usually supplied together with the main and big-end bearings on a reground crankshaft.

6 If the spigot bearing in the rear of the crankshaft requires renewal extract it with a suitable puller. Alternatively fill it with heavy grease and use a close fitting dowel driven into the centre of the bearing. Refitting of this bearing must be left until after the crankshaft machining and cleaning tasks are completed. Ensure that the replacement bearing is of the correct size to suit the diameter of the crankshaft pilot bore and the transmission input shaft, as different types have been used. If in doubt, get a Ford dealer to advise accordingly. Drive the new bearing into position using a suitable soft metal drift (photo).

25.2A Flattened Plastigage filament (arrowed)

25.2B Checking the width of filament against the scale on the packet

25.4A Bearing shell identification number (typical)

25.4B Crankshaft paintmark (arrowed) indicates undersize bearings fitted during manufacture – check with Ford dealer

25.6 Crankshaft spigot (pilot) bearing

26.3 Pump oil through oilways in crankshaft to check for signs of dirt and/or machining swarf

7   Before taking the crankshaft for regrinding, check also the cylinder bores and pistons, as it may be advantageous to have the whole engine reconditioned together.

26   Crankshaft main and big-end bearing shells – examination and renovation

1   With careful servicing and regular oil and filter changes, bearings will last for a very long time, but they can still fail for unforeseen reasons. With big-end bearings the indication is a regular rhythmic knocking from the crankcase. The frequency depends on engine speed and is particularly noticeable when the engine is under load. This symptom is accompanied by a fall in oil pressure, although this is not normally noticeable unless an oil pressure gauge is fitted. Main bearing failure is usually indicated by serious vibration, particularly at higher engine revolutions, accompanied by a more significant drop in oil pressure and a 'rumbling' noise.

2   Bearing shells in good condition have bearing surfaces with a smooth, even matt silver/grey colour all over. Worn bearings will show patches of a different colour when the bearing metal has worn away and exposed the underlay. Damaged bearings will be pitted or scored. It is always well worthwhile fitting new shells as their cost is relatively low. If the crankshaft is in good condition it is merely a question of obtaining another set of standard size shells. A reground crankshaft will need new bearing shells as a matter of course.

3   Squirt clean engine oil through the crankshaft oilways to ensure that they are clear and clean of any machining swarf (photo).

27   Cylinder block/crankcase – examination and renovation

1   A new cylinder is perfectly round and the walls parallel throughout its length. The action of the piston tends to wear the walls at right-angles to the gudgeon pin due to side thrust. This wear takes place principally on that section of the cylinder swept by the piston rings.

2   It is possible to get an indication of bore wear by removing the cylinder head with the engine still in the car. With the piston down in the bore first signs of wear can be seen and felt just below the top of the bore where the top piston ring reaches and there will be a noticeable lip. If there is no lip it is fairly reasonable to expect that bore wear is not

severe and any lack of compression or excessive oil consumption is due to worn or broken piston rings or pistons (see the next Section).

3   If it is possible to obtain a bore-measuring micrometer, measure the bore in the thrust plane below the lip and again at the bottom of the cylinder in the same plane. If the difference is greater than 0.015 mm (0.006 in), it will be necessary in the case of the 2.1 litre engine to fit new cylinder liners and matching piston assemblies. Similarly, a greater than 0.08 mm (0.003 in) difference in measurement across the bore indicates ovality and calls for the same treatment.

4   Any bore which is significantly scratched or scored will need renewing. This symptom usually indicates that the piston or rings are damaged. In the event of only one cylinder being in need of liner renewal, it is considered best for a complete set of four to be fitted.

5   The old liners can be driven upwards from the cylinder block using a suitable wooden block (Fig. 1.9). If the crankshaft is undergoing regrinding, it is a good idea to let the same firm renew the liners, and renovate and reassemble the crankshaft and pistons to the block. A reputable firm normally gives a guarantee for such work.

6   In the case of the 2.3 and 2.5 litre engines the cylinder bores are machined directly in the cylinder block, and liners are not fitted. Should the cylinder bores of these engines be worn, scored or oval, the cylinder may be rebored and oversize pistons fitted. Again this work must be carried out by a specialist firm who will decide how much metal must be

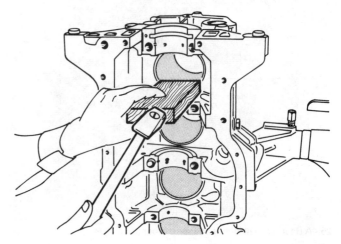

Fig. 1.9 Removing a cylinder liner from the 2.1 litre engine (Sec 27)

27.8 Inspect the condition of the core plugs

28.1 Remove circlips to allow gudgeon pin withdrawal

ground off the cylinder bores, and will supply a set of oversize pistons and piston rings to suit.

7   If new standard size pistons and/or rings are being fitted and the cylinders have not been rebored or had new liners fitted, it is essential to slightly roughen the hard glaze on the sides of the bores with fine emery so the new piston rings will have a chance to bed in properly. The top piston ring will also have to be of the 'stepped' type to avoid fouling the unworn ridge at the top of the cylinder bore.

8   Examine the crankcase for cracks and leaking core plugs. To renew a core plug, drill a hole in its centre and tap a thread in it. Screw in a bolt and, using a distance piece, tighten the bolt and extract the core plug. When fitting the new plug, smear its outer edge with gasket cement (photo).

9   Squirt clean engine oil through the various oil galleries using a pump action oil gun to ensure that the oilways are clear. Also check that the coolant galleries are clear.

10   Turbo models have an oil splash nozzle fitted at the base of each cylinder bore and their function is to cool the underside of the pistons by spraying them with oil. Ensure that the nozzles are clean and, if removed, renew their retaining bolt washers (Fig. 1.7).

28 Piston/connecting rod assemblies – examination and renovation

1   Using a pair of circlip pliers, remove the circlips from the piston (photo) and slide out the gudgeon pin from the piston and connecting rod small-end bearing. If the gudgeon pin is a tight fit, immerse the piston in hot water. The gudgeon pin should then slide out quite easily. Mark the connecting rod in relation to the piston so that it may be refitted in exactly the same way.

2   To remove the piston rings, slide them carefully over the top of the piston, taking care not to scratch the aluminium alloy of the piston. Never slide them off the bottom of the piston skirt. It is very easy to break piston rings if they are pulled off roughly, so this operation should be done with extreme caution. It is helpful to use an old feeler gauge to facilitate their removal as follows.

3   Lift one end of the piston ring to be removed out of its groove and insert the end of the feeler gauge under it.

4   Turn the feeler gauge slowly round the piston; as the ring comes out of its groove it rests on the land above. It can then be eased off the piston with the feeler gauge stopping it from slipping into any empty grooves, if it is any but the top piston ring that is being removed.

5   Piston ring wear can be checked by first removing the rings from the pistons as described previously. Place each ring in the cylinder bores individually from the top and push them down the bores approximately 38 mm (1.5 in) with the head of a piston, so that they rest square in the cylinder. Then measure the gap at the ends of the rings with a feeler gauge. If the gap exceeds the figures given in the Specifications the rings will need renewal (photo).

6   Clean out the piston ring grooves using a piece of old piston ring as a scraper. Be careful not to scratch the aluminium surface of the pistons.

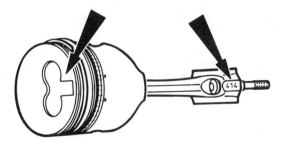

Fig. 1.10 Piston to connecting rod orientation (Sec 28)

28.5 Checking a piston ring gap

29.3 Inspect the camshaft lobes, oil pump drive gear teeth and bearing surfaces for signs of excessive wear or damage

30.0 Inspect the tappets for excessive wear

with fine emery. The cam lobes however, are surface hardened, and once this is penetrated wear will be very rapid thereafter (photo).

Protect your fingers – piston ring edges are sharp. Also probe the groove oil return holes.

7   The grooves in which the rings locate in the piston become enlarged in use. If the clearance between ring and piston in the piston ring groove is other than minimal, the piston and rings must be renewed.

8   Examine the connecting rods carefully. They are not subject to wear, but in extreme cases such as partial engine seizure they could be distorted. Such conditions may be visually apparent, but if doubt exists they should be renewed, or checked for alignment by engine reconditioning specialists. If new gudgeon pin bushes are required, this job should also be entrusted to a specialist as the new bushes have to be reamed to fit the gudgeon pins.

9   If new pistons are being fitted they will be supplied with the rings already assembled. If new rings are to be fitted to existing pistons, follow the manufacturer's fitting instructions supplied with the rings. Note that when fitting new standard size pistons and/or rings to partially worn cylinders, the top ring will need to be of the 'stepped' type to avoid fouling the unworn ridge at the top of the cylinder bore.

10   Refitting the piston to the connecting rod is the reverse sequence to removal, ensuring that the two components are refitted the same way as noted during dismantling (Fig. 1.10).

29   Camshaft and camshaft bearings – examination and renovation

1   The camshaft bearing bushes should be examined for signs of scoring and pitting. If they need renewal they will have to be dealt with professionally as, although it may be relatively easy to remove the old bushes, the correct fitting of new ones requires special tools. If they are not fitted evenly and square they will wear in a very short time. See your Ford garage or local engineering specialist for this work.

2   The camshaft itself may show signs of wear on the bearing journals, cam lobes or the skew gear. The main decision to take is what degree of wear justifies renewal, which is costly. Any signs of scoring or damage to the bearing journals cannot be remedied by regrinding. Renewal of the whole camshaft is the only solution. Similarly, excessive wear on the skew gear which can be seen where the oil pump driveshaft teeth mesh will mean renewal of the whole camshaft.

3   The cam lobes themselves may show signs of ridging or pitting on the high points. If ridging is light then it may be possible to smooth it out

30   Tappets – examination

The faces of the tappets which bear on the camshaft should show no signs of pitting, scoring or other forms of wear. Thoroughly clean them out, removing all traces of sludge. It is most unlikely that the sides of the tappets will prove worn, but if they are a very loose fit in their bores and can be rocked readily, then they should be exchanged for new units. It is very unusual to find any wear in the tappets, and any wear present is likely to occur only at very high mileages (photo).

31   Timing components – examination and renovation

2.1 litre engine
1   The 2.1 litre engine is equipped with gear-driven timing components which are very robust and it is unlikely that any wear will have taken place. Check, however, that the teeth are sound with no signs of chipping or pitting that would indicate a breakdown of the surface hardening.

2   Renew any gears that show signs of wear, referring to paragraph 5 of this Section if the camshaft gear requires renewal (photo).

2.3 and 2.5 litre engines
3   Carefully examine the teeth of the crankshaft, camshaft, fuel injection pump and idler gear sprockets. Check the camshaft endfloat as shown (photos).

4   Each tooth forms an inverted 'V' with the sprocket periphery, and if worn the side of each tooth (ie one side of the inverted 'V') will be concave when compared with the other. If any sign of wear is present the sprockets must be renewed.

5   Should the camshaft sprocket be worn, the use of a press will be required to remove and refit the sprocket. When refitting, heat the sprocket in well-heated oil and then press it on the camshaft until the specified endfloat clearance exists between the sprocket and the interface plate (photo).

6   If any of the timing sprockets are to be renewed it will also be necessary to replace the crankshaft sprocket with one having the correct timing reference dot on its front face directly opposite the Woodruff keyway.

31.2 Check the camshaft thrust plate-to-gear clearance on the 2.1 litre engine

31.3A Examine the sprocket teeth for excessive wear (2.3 and 2.5 litre engines) and ...

31.3B ... check the camshaft endfloat

31.5 Camshaft and sprocket

7   Examine the links of the chain for side slackness, and renew the chain if any slackness is noticeable when compared with a new chain. It is a sensible precaution to renew the chain at about 30 000 miles (48 000 km) and at a lesser mileage if the engine is stripped down for a major overhaul. The actual rollers on a very badly worn chain may be slightly grooved.

8   Carefully inspect the timing chain tensioner thrust pad, and if it is badly grooved it must be renewed. Also check that the plunger is free to move in and out with no signs of sticking.

9   Renew the timing cover oil seal. Drive or press out the old seal (noting its orientation), clean the housing, then drive or press the new seal into position (see photo 6.11).

32   Rockers and rocker shaft – examination and renovation

1   Lift out the end post retaining bolt and then slide the end post, rockers, springs and pedestals off the rocker shaft, noting their positioning and keeping them in order as they are removed (photos).

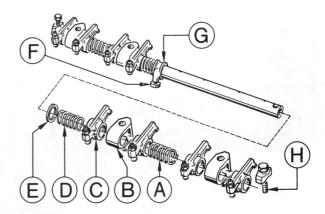

Fig. 1.11 Rocker shaft assembly (Sec 32)

A   Long spring
B   Bearing pedestal
C   Rocker
D   Short spring
E   Support plate
F   Seal
G   Lubrication collar
H   Outer pedestal bolt

32.1A Remove the end post bolt ...

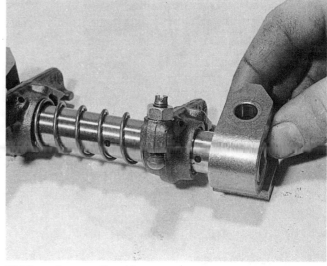

32.1B ... and remove the end post ...

32.1C ... rockers and spring assemblies

32.4 Inspect the rocker bushes for excessive wear

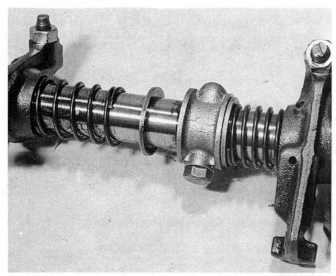

32.6 Thrustwashers are fitted against the lubrication collar (each side)

2   The lubrication collar on the centre of the shaft can be removed after withdrawing the locating bolt.

3   Check the shaft for straightness by rolling it on a flat surface. It is most unlikely that it will be bent, but if it is then a judicious attempt must be made to straighten it. If this is not successful a new shaft must be obtained. The surface of the shaft must be free from any worn ridges caused by the rocker arms. If any wear is evident renew the shaft. Wear is only likely to have occurred if the rocker shaft oil holes have become blocked.

4   Check the rocker arms for wear of the rocker bushes, for wear at the rocker arm face which bears on the valve stem, and for wear of the adjusting ball-ended screws. Wear in the rocker arm bush can be checked by gripping the rocker arm tip and holding the rocker arm in place on the shaft, noting if there is any lateral rocker arm shake. If shake is present, and the arms are very loose on the shaft, a new bush or rocker arm must be fitted (photo).

5   Check the top of the rocker arm where it bears on the valve head for cracking or serious wear of the case hardening. If none is present, re-use the rocker arm. Check the lower half of the ball on the end of the rocker arm adjusting screw. On high mileage engines, wear on the ball and top

of the pushrod is easily noted by the unworn 'pip' which fits in the small central oil hole on the ball. The larger this 'pip' the more wear has taken place to both the ball and the pushrod. Check the pushrods for straightness by rolling them on a flat surface. Renew any that are bent.

6   Reassemble the rockers and the associated fittings to the shaft. Lubricate them with engine oil as they are fitted and ensure that they are refitted in the correct order, remembering to locate the thrustwasher each side of the lubrication collar (photo).

33 Flywheel – examination and renovation

1   Examine the clutch disc mating surface of the flywheel. If this is deeply grooved or scored the flywheel must be renewed.

2   If the teeth on the starter ring gear are badly worn or some are missing, then it will be necessary to remove the ring gear. The old ring can be removed from the flywheel by cutting a notch between two teeth with a hacksaw and then splitting it with a cold chisel. Take suitable precautions to avoid flying fragments, paying particular attention to protection of the eyes. Note which way round the rig gear is fitted!

3   To fit a new ring gear requires heating the ring to 400°F (204°C). This can be done by polishing four equally spaced sections of the gear, laying it on a suitable heat resistant surface (such as fire bricks) and heating it evenly with a blow torch or lamp until the polished areas turn a light yellow tinge. *Do not overheat*, or the hard wearing properties will be lost. When hot enough place the gear in position quickly, tapping it home if necessary, and let it cool naturally without quenching in any way.

34 Cylinder head and piston crowns – decarbonising

1   With the cylinder head off, carefully remove with a wire brush and blunt scraper all traces of carbon deposits from the combustion spaces and the ports. The valve heads, stems and valve guides should also be freed from any carbon deposits. Wash the combustion spaces and ports down with petrol and scrape the cylinder head surface free of any foreign matter with the side of a steel rule, or a similar surface.

2   Clean the pistons and top of the cylinder bores (photo). If the pistons are still in the block, then it is essential that great care is taken to ensure

34.2 Piston crown cleaned for inspection

that no carbon gets into the cylinder bores, as this could scratch the cylinder walls or cause damage to the pistons and rings. To ensure this does not happen, first turn the crankshaft so that two of the pistons are at the top of their bores. Stuff rag into the other two bores, or seal them off with paper and masking tape. The waterways should also be covered with small pieces of masking tape to prevent particles of carbon entering the cooling system and damaging the water pump.

3   There are two schools of thought as to how much carbon should be removed from the piston crown. One school recommends that a ring of carbon should be left around the edge of the piston and on the cylinder bore wall as an aid to low oil consumption. Although this is probably true for old engines with worn bores, on newer engines the thought of the second school can be applied, which is that for effective decarbonisation, all traces of carbon should be removed. If all traces of carbon are to be removed, press a little grease into the gap between the cylinder walls and the two pistons which are to be worked on. With a blunt scraper, carefully scrape away the carbon from the piston crown, taking great care not to scratch the aluminium. Also scrape away the carbon from the surrounding lip of the cylinder wall. When all carbon has been removed, scrape away all the grease which will now be contaminated with carbon particles, taking care not to press any into the bores. To assist prevention of carbon build-up, the piston crown can be polished with a metal polish. Remove the rags or masking tape from the other two cylinders, and turn the crankshaft so that the two pistons which were at the bottom are now at the top. Place rag or masking tape in the cylinders which have been decarbonised and proceed as just described.

4   If a ring of carbon is going to be left round the piston, then this can be helped by inserting an old piston ring into the top of the bore to rest on the piston and ensure that carbon is not accidentally removed.

5   Check that there are no particles of carbon in the cylinder bores. Decarbonising is now complete.

6   Renovation of the valves and valve seats is described in the following Section.

7   When ordering any replacement parts, it is important that a new head gasket of the correct thickness is obtained. Refer to Section 49 for details.

35 Valves and valve seats – examination and renovation

1   Examine the heads of the valves for pitting and burning, especially the heads of the exhaust valves. The valve seats should be examined at the same time. If the pitting on valve and seat is very slight, the marks can be removed by grinding the seats and valves together with fine grinding paste. Where bad pitting has occurred to the valve seats. It will be necessary to recut them and fit new valves. If the valve seats are so worn that they cannot be recut, then it will be necessary to fit new valve seat inserts. These latter two jobs should be entrusted to the local Ford dealer or engineering works. In practice, it is very seldom that the seats are so badly worn that they require renewal. Normally, it is the exhaust valve that is too badly worn for refitting, and the owner can easily purchase a new set of valves and match them to the seats by valve grinding.

2   The cylinder head, valves and valve seat inserts were modified in April 1984 and when renewing any of these components (individually or collectively), it is essential that replacements are of the correct type. The latter type cylinder head can be fitted to earlier models when fitted with the later type valves and seats, but prior to renewing any of these components, consult your local Ford dealer for clarification of the correct replacement parts required.

3   Valve grinding is carried out as follows. Smear a trace of fine carborundum paste on the seat face and apply a suction grinder tool to the valve head. With semi-rotary motion, grind the valve head to its seat, lifting the valve occasionally to redistribute the grinding paste.

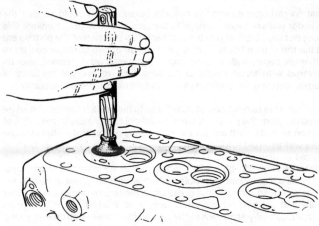

Fig. 1.12 Regrinding a valve/seat face (Sec 35)

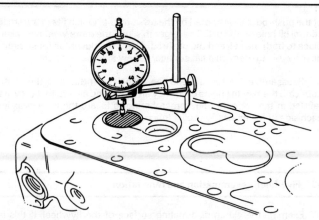

Fig. 1.13 Method used to measure valve head depth in cylinder head (Sec 35)

When a smooth unbroken ring of light grey matt finish is produced, on both valve and valve seat faces, the grinding operation is completed (Fig. 1.12).

4   Scrape away all carbon from the valve head and the valve stem. Carefully clean away every trace of grinding compound, taking care to leave none in the ports or in the valve guides. Clean the valves and valve seats with a paraffin soaked rag, then with a clean rag, and finally, if an air line is available, blow the valves, valve guides and valve ports clean.

5   As each valve is ground in, check that the valve face to cylinder head surface (valve head depth) is within the specified tolerance for the model in question (Fig. 1.13).

36 Valve guides and swirl chambers – examination

1   Examine the valve guides internally for wear. If the valves are a very loose fit in the guides and there is the slightest suspicion of lateral rocking using a new valve, then the guide will have to be reamed and oversize valves fitted. This is a job best left to the local Ford dealer.

2   Check the swirl chambers for security of fit, excessive cracking and distortion. Small cracks may be evident around the fuel outlet, but these are acceptable and will not affect the operation of the engine. It is not normally necessary to remove the swirl chambers from the cylinder head unless there are obvious signs of damage. If this is the case this work should also be entrusted to your Ford dealer.

3   It should be noted that the swirl chambers and the cylinder head on later 2.5 litre models were modified so that the ball in the swirl chamber and the corresponding groove in the cylinder head were relocated by 180° (the groove now being on the valve side). If the swirl chambers are to be renewed it is therefore important to ensure that the correct replacements are obtained.

37 Sump – examination

Wash out the oil sump and wipe dry. Inspect the exterior for signs of damage or excessive rust. If evident, a new oil sump must be obtained. To ensure an oil tight joint, scrape away all traces of the old gasket from the cylinder block mating face.

38 Engine – reassembly (general)

1   To ensure maximum life with minimum trouble from a rebuilt engine, not only must everything be correctly assembled, but everything must be spotlessly clean, all the oilways must be clear, locking washers and spring washers must always be fitted where indicated, and all bearing and other working surfaces must be thoroughly lubricated during assembly.

2   Before assembly begins, renew any bolts or studs the threads of which are in any way damaged, and whenever possible use new washers.

3   In addition to the normal range of good quality socket spanners and general tools which are essential; the following must be available before assembly begins:

   (a)   Complete set of new gaskets
   (b)   Supply of clean rag
   (c)   Clean oil can full of engine oil
   (d)   Torque wrench
   (e)   All new parts as necessary

4   One point worth noting is that there are two types of cylinder head gasket available for the 2.3 and 2.5 litre engines. The correct gasket to be fitted is determined by the amount of protrusion above the mating face of the cylinder block. It will therefore be necessary to assemble the crankshaft, pistons and connecting rods to enable a measurement of piston protrusion to be taken before obtaining the cylinder head gasket.

5   The engine shown in the photographs is the 2.3 litre type and differs in minor ways from the other two diesel engines used in this Ford range. Provided that care is taken to note any differences between the text and the actual engine being worked on during dismantling, no problems will arise.

39 Crankshaft and main bearings – refitting

1   Ensure that the crankcase and crankshaft are thoroughly clean and the oilways clear. Inject clean engine oil into the crankshaft oilways. On Turbo models, refit the oil nozzles to the base of each cylinder using new seal washers. Tighten the retaining bolts to the specified torque setting.

2   Commence the work of rebuilding the engine by fitting the two composite half oil seals into the grooves adjacent to the crankcase rear main bearing journal and rear main bearing cap (photo).

3   Ensure that the seal is pushed fully home into its groove but without excessively compressing it. A wooden dowel or hammer handle is useful for carefully rolling the seal into position. After fitting cut the seal ends so that they are perfectly flush with the mating surfaces of the crankcase and bearing cap (photo).

4   Now wipe the main bearing shell locations in the crankcase with a soft non-fluffy rag.

5   Fit the five upper halves of the main bearing shells into their locations in the crankcase ensuring that the notches on the shells engage with the slots in the crankcase (photo).

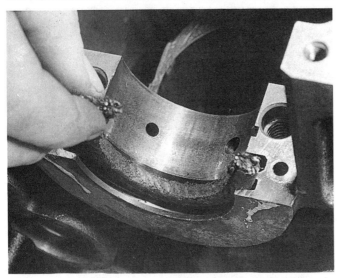

39.2 Locate the half seals into the rear main bearing journal groove ...

39.3 ... and trim off flush with block face

39.5 Locate the main bearing upper half shells

39.6 Fit the thrustwashers each side of the centre main bearing journal

39.7 Lower the crankshaft into position

6   Apply a little grease to the two thrustwasher halves and position them either side of the crankcase centre main bearing journal. Note that the dimpled side faces the crankshaft (photo).

7   Thoroughly lubricate the five main bearing shells and then carefully lower the crankshaft into position (photo).

8   Fit the main bearing shell lower halves to each main bearing cap and then lay them out beside the crankcase.

9   Apply a little grease to the remaining two thrustwashers and then position them on the centre main bearing cap, dimpled side toward the crankshaft.

10   Thoroughly lubricate the crankshaft centre main bearing journal and then fit the centre main bearing cap and thrustwashers to the crankcase. **Note:** *The notches on the crankcase and bearing cap that accept the tags on the bearing shells must be on the same side (photo).*

11   Refit the centre main bearing cap retaining and progressively tighten them to half their specified torque wrench setting.

12   Move the crankshaft as far as it will go to the rear and then, using feeler gauges, measure the clearance between the thrustwashers and

39.10 Fit the centre main bearing cap and thrustwashers

39.12 Check the crankshaft endfloat

39.13 Locate the lateral oil seals to the rear main bearing cap ...

39.14 ... then fit the bearing cap (with seals)

the side of the crankshaft journal (photo). This is the crankshaft endfloat, and if it is outside the limits shown in the Specifications, oversize thrustwashers must be fitted.

13   The rear main bearing cap lateral oil seals can now be installed. Position the seals in the groove on either side of the cap, ensuring that the head of the seal engages with the dowel pin on the cap (photo).

14   Smear a little grease on the seals, lubricate the crankshaft rear journal, and then carefully lower the rear main bearing cap into position (photo). Ease the cap and seals down by hand, holding the seals in place with your fingers. When the cap is fully home, refit the retaining bolts tightened to half the specified torque wrench setting only.

15   Fit the remaining main bearing caps, tightening the retaining bolts to half the specified torque wrench setting only at this stage.

16   Now fully tighten the retaining bolts of each main bearing cap in turn to the specified torque wrench setting (photo). Check that the crankshaft is free to turn after tightening each cap. Should it be excessively stiff to turn, or possess high spots, a most careful inspection must be made with a micrometer, preferably by a qualified mechanic to get to the root of the trouble. However, it is very seldom that problems of this nature will be experienced when fitting the crankshaft.

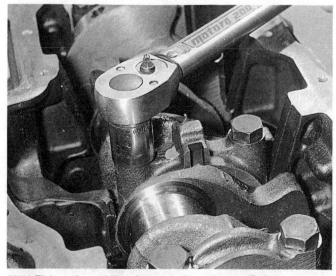

39.16 Tighten the main bearing cap bolts to the specified torque setting

39.17 Trim off the lateral seals leaving the specified protrusion

39.18 Insert the tappets into their bores (2,3 and 2.5 litre engines)

17   After fully tightening all the main bearing bolts, trim off the protruding ends of the lateral oil seals using a sharp knife so that 0.5 mm (0.01 in) is left protruding (photo).

18   On 2.3 and 2.5 litre models, insert the respective tappets into their bores in the cylinder block. Smear them with grease to prevent them from falling out during subsequent operations before the camshaft is fitted (photo).

40   Cylinder liners (2.1 litre engine) – refitting

1   Before fitting the cylinder liners into the cylinder block, first ensure that the mating faces of each are clean.

2   Insert the liners without their rubber seal into their respective positions in the cylinder block, ensure that they are fully seated then clamp them in position in the manner described in Section 7.

3   Clamp a suitable dial gauge to the top face of the cylinder block and measure the protrusion of each liner in turn (from the top face of the cylinder block). Each liner must be within the specified limit, if not check the seatings (Fig. 1.14).

4   Unclamp and remove the liners, fit a new O-ring seal to the bottom end of each, then refit each liner in turn into its appropriate position in

the cylinder block. Refit the liner clamps ensuring that they do not overlap the cylinder bores (Fig. 1.15).

41   Pistons and connecting rods – refitting

1   The pistons and their respective connecting rods can now be fitted to their respective bores. Commence by cleaning the backs of the bearing shells and the recesses in the connecting rods and big-end bearing caps.

2   Place the big-end bearing shells in position on the connecting rods and caps, with the notches on the bearing shells engaged in the groove of the rod and cap.

3   Wipe clean the cylinder bores with a non-fluffy rag, then liberally lubricate them with engine oil.

4   Position the piston rings so that their gaps are 120° apart from each other and then lubricate the pistons and piston rings.

5   Insert one of the connecting rod and piston assemblies into the top of the cylinder bore, ensuring that it is the correct way round (the cutaway portion on the piston crown toward the left-hand side of the cylinder block).

6   Before pushing the piston fully into its bore, compress the piston rings using a piston ring compressor (photo), and then tap the piston

Fig. 1.14 Method used to measure the cylinder liner protrusion on the 2.1 litre engine (Sec 40)

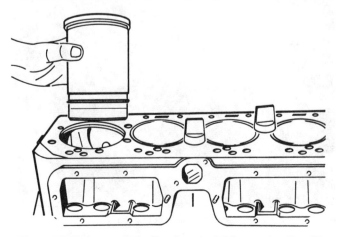

Fig. 1.15 Refitting a cylinder liner into the 2.1 litre engine (Sec 40)

41.6A Fitting a piston/connecting rod with the aid of a ring compressor

41.6B Fully fitted piston showing correct orientation

41.8 Locate the big-end bearing caps ...

41.9 ... and tighten their retaining nuts to the specified torque setting

41.11 Check the endfloat of each connecting rod

41.12 Check the crankshaft frictional moment (torque)

firmly into the cylinder bore using a block of wood against the centre of the piston crown (photos).

7 With the crankshaft journal at its lowest point, continue pushing the piston down the bore until the connecting rod and bearing shell are firmly seated on the crankshaft journal.

8 Lubricate the crankshaft journal and then assemble the big-end bearing cap and shell onto the connecting rod, with the notches of the shells on adjacent sides (photos).

9 Refit the retaining nuts and tighten them to the torque figure given in the Specifications (photo).

10 Repeat the foregoing operations on the remaining three piston and connecting rod assemblies.

11 Use a feeler gauge and check that the endfloat of each connecting rod at the big-end is within the specified limits (photo).

12 The crankshaft frictional moment (torque) should now be measured. To achieve this, connect a torque wrench to the bolt in the front end of the crankshaft and measure the moment of friction at which the crankshaft starts to rotate. This must not be exceed 60 Nm (43 lbf ft) (photo).

42 Camshaft – refitting

2.1 litre engine

1 Wipe the front face of the cylinder block with a non-fluffy rag and then place a new gasket in position (photo).

2 Make sure that the mating surface of the front interface plate is clean and free of any traces of old gasket.

3 Now position the interface plate on the front of the engine and secure it in position using only the bolts which are not also used for securing the timing cover (photo).

4 Wipe the camshaft and camshaft bearings clean and then liberally lubricate them with engine oil.

5 Carefully insert the camshaft into the cylinder block, taking care not to damage the bearing surfaces with the sharp edges of the cam lobes. Tighten the camshaft thrust plate bolts to the specified torque setting (photos).

6 The tappets can be lubricated and fitted into their respective bores in the cylinder block at this stage (photo) or left until later when fitting the pushrods.

42.1 Place a new gasket on the front face of the cylinder block (2.1 litre engine) ...

42.3 ... then fit the front interface plate

42.5A Insert the camshaft ...

42.5B ... and refit the thrust plate retaining bolts

42.6 Insert the cam followers into their original bores (2.1 litre)

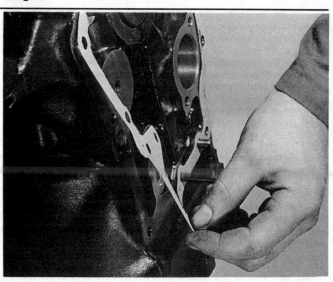

42.8 Locate a new gasket onto the engine front face (2.3 and 2.5 litre engines) ...

42.9A ... refit the camshaft and interface plate ...

42.9B ... with the plate engaged in the groove (arrowed)

2.3 and 2.5 litre engines

7　Check that the mating faces of the cylinder block and the interface plate are clean. Also check that the tappets are fully located in their bores in the cylinder block (if protruding, they can prevent the camshaft from being fully inserted).

8　Smear the mating face of the new interface gasket with grease then stick it in position on the front face of the engine (photo).

9　Partially insert the camshaft into the cylinder block, then engage the interface plate over it and locate it in the groove between the camshaft sprocket and the shoulder of the camshaft. Line up the interface plate with the dowels in the block, then fully fit the camshaft and the interface plate. Fit and tighten the four interface plate retaining bolts to the specified torque wrench setting (photos).

43 Oil pump – refitting

1　Position the oil pump so that the grub screw locating hole is toward the side of the engine (photo) and then slide the oil pump into position in the crankcase.

42.9C Tighten the interface bolts to the specified torque setting

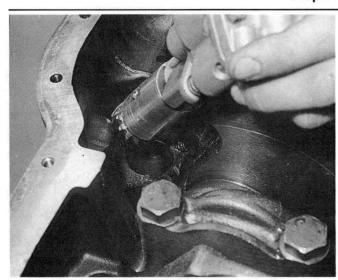

43.1 Insert the oil pump unit ...

43.3 ... and fit the grub screw to secure the oil pump ...

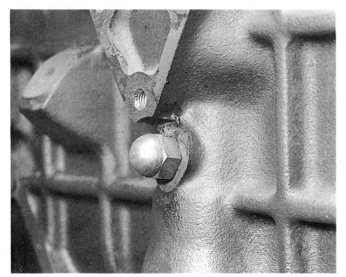

43.4 ... then fit the domed locknut

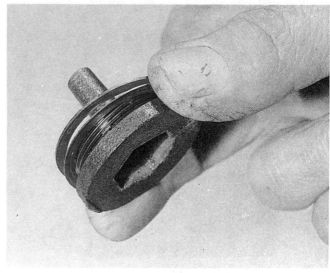

43.5A Locate the shims over the thrust plug ...

43.5B ... then fit the plug

2   Push the oil pump fully home until the drive gear meshes with the gear on the camshaft, and the locating hole on the pump body is visibly in line with the grub screw hole on the side of the cylinder block.

3   Using a small Allen key, screw the grub screw into position making sure that it engages with the pump (photo).

4   Now refit the domed locknut to the grub screw (photo).

5   Install the retaining/thrust plug and shims and tighten the plug to specified torque by reversing its removal procedure (photos) – see Section 19.

44   Sump – refitting

1   Ensure that the mating surfaces of the sump and crankcase are clean and free from any traces of old gasket material.

2   Coat both sides of a new sump gasket with grease and place the gasket in position on the crankcase (photo).

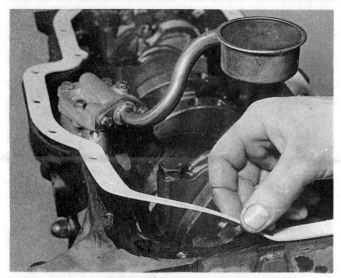

44.2 Locate the sump gasket ...

44.3A ... fit the sump ...

3   Place the sump in position and refit the retaining bolts. Tighten the retaining bolts (and the two nuts to the base of the interface plate) in a progressive sequence to the specified torque wrench setting (photos).

44.3B ... and tighten the retaining bolts (and nuts) to the specified torque setting

45 Flywheel – refitting

1   Locate the rear interface plate over the dowels on the rear face of the engine (photo).

2   Place the flywheel in position over the rear face of the crankshaft and line up the marks made during removal.

3   If applicable, fit a new lock plate. Refit the flywheel retaining bolts and tighten them in a diagonal and progressive sequence to the specified torque wrench setting for the model. Where applicable, bend the locktabs of the lockplate over the bolt heads to secure them (photos).

45.1 Engage the rear plate over the location dowels

45.3A Fit the flywheel and retaining bolts ...

45.3B ... lock the starter ring gear ...

45.3C ... then tighten the flywheel bolts to the specified torque setting

45.3D Bend the locktabs over to secure the bolts (where applicable)

46 Timing components – refitting (engine out of car)

2.1 litre engine (with gear-driven timing components)

1   Rotate the crankshaft until Nos 1 and 4 pistons are at the TDC position.

2   Refit the Woodruff key to the crankshaft and then slide on the crankshaft gear with the raised centre boss toward the engine (photos).

3   Place the fuel injection pump complete with drive gear in position and secure it with the lower rear mounting bolt only at this stage (photo).

4   Now turn the camshaft and fuel injection pump gears as necessary, and then slide on the idler gear so that when fitted the timing marks on all four gears are in line (photos).

5   Refit the thrustwasher and circlip to the idler gear (photo).

6   If any of the timing gears have been renewed, it will be necessary to have the fuel injection pump timing checked, and if necessary reset, by your Ford dealer after the engine has been initially started and run for a short while (see Chapter 3).

46.2A Locate the Woodruff keys into their grooves in the crankshaft ...

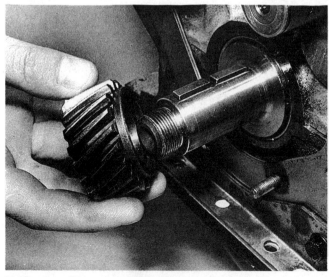

46.2B ... then slide on the crankshaft gear (2.1 litre engine)

46.3 Fuel injector pump and gear in position (2.1 litre engine)

46.4A Refit the idler gear ...

46.4B ... ensuring timing marks (arrowed) of all gears are in alignment as indicated (2.1 litre engine)

46.5 Idler gear thrustwasher and circlip (2.1 litre engine)

46.8A Engage the inner Woodruff key into its groove in the crankshaft ...

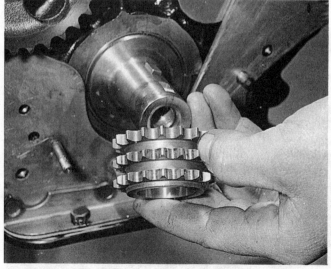

46.8B ... then fit the crankshaft sprocket (2.3 and 2.5 litre engines)

46.9 Fit the idler sprocket (2.3 and 2.5 litre engines)

2.3 and 2.5 litre engines (with chain-driven timing components)

7   Rotate the crankshaft until Nos 1 and 4 pistons are at their TDC position.

8   Refit the Woodruff key to the crankshaft and then slide on the crankshaft sprocket (photos).

9   Refit the idler sprocket and semi-tighten its retaining bolt. At this stage, set the sprocket at the minimum adjustment position (photo).

10   Lubricate and fit the oil seals to the injection pump/sprocket bearing housing, then locate the housing into position in the interface plate with the retaining bolt loosely fitted. Now refit the pump bearing oil delivery pipe to the interface plate and the pump bearing/sprocket housing and fully tighten the retaining bolts. Ensure that the rebated side of the bolt hole in the oil pipe faces towards the interface plate (photos).

11   Smear the timing cover gasket with grease or sealant and locate it on the front face of the interface plate. Although this gasket can be fitted later after the timing chain has been fitted (as shown in our photos), it is easier to locate it at this stage.

46.10A Locate the O-ring seal ...

46.10B ... and the small rubber collar seal to the injection pump/sprocket bearing housing (2.3 and 2.5 litre engines)

46.10C Fit the bearing housing to the interface plate ...

46.10D ... together with the oil pipe and bolt (2.3 and 2.5 litre engines)

46.12 Fit the injection pump drive sprocket (2.3 and 2.5 litre engines)

46.13B Showing crankshaft sprocket with keyway at TDC and timing mark on chain aligned as required (2.3 and 2.5 litre engines)

46.14A Locate the gasket ...

46.13A Timing chain and sprockets showing timing mark alignment points (arrowed) – 2.3 and 2.5 litre engines

12   Locate the injection pump drive sprocket into its bearing housing (photo), check that the crankshaft sprocket is still set at the TDC position, then hold the timing chain against the crankshaft, camshaft and injection pump drive sprockets and align the timing marks on the chain with the corresponding timing marks on the sprockets.

13   Withdraw the injection pump sprocket from its bearing housing, insert it into engagement with the timing chain so that the timing mark of the sprocket and chain align, then refit the sprocket to the bearing housing and simultaneously engage the chain over the crankshaft, camshaft and idler sprockets. When engaged over the sprockets, check that the relevant timing marks of the chain and sprockets are in alignment (photo).

14   Refit the chain tensioner unit onto the front face of the interface plate and secure with the retaining bolt and nut. Release the retractor lock in the tensioner (photos).

15   Insert an Allen key into the hole in the idler sprocket eccentric arm and turn the arm to give a clearance 0.5 to 1.0 mm (0.019 to 0.040 in) between the adjuster shoe and carrier, then tighten the idler sprocket bolt to set the tension (photos).

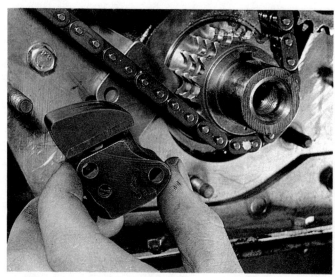

46.14B ... and fit the chain tensioner ...

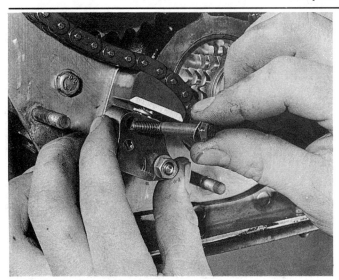

46.14C ... retaining bolt and nut ...

46.14D ... then unlock the retractor in the lock (2.3 and 2.5 litre engines)

46.15A Adjust the idler sprocket eccentric arm to provide ...

46.15B ... the specified clearance between the tensioner shoe and carrier (2.3 and 2.5 litre engines)

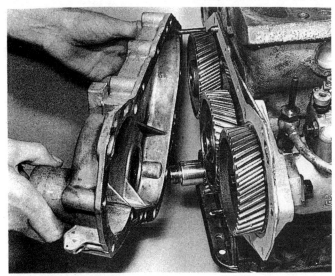

47.4A Timing cover refitting – 2.1 litre engines

47.4B Timing cover refitting – 2.3 litre engine

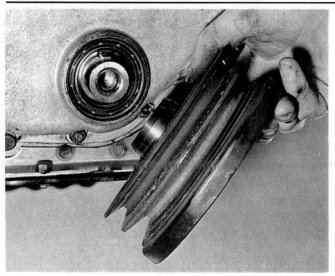

47.5 Fit the pulley onto the crankshaft

47.7 Tighten retaining bolt to specified torque (2.3 litre engine shown)

47   Timing cover – refitting (engine out of car)

1   Ensure that the mating surfaces of the timing cover and front interface are clean and free from any traces of old gasket. Smear some grease or sealant onto both faces of the new cover gasket and then carefully locate it into position against the interface. On models with chain-driven timing components (2.3 and 2.5 litre engines), the gasket may already have been fitted as suggested in the previous Section, but if not, take care as the gasket is passed over the chain and sprockets and onto the front studs – it may easily split.

2   Lubricate the timing gears or chain and sprockets (as applicable) with clean engine oil.

3   Insert the crankshaft pulley Woodruff key into the slot in the crankshaft.

4   Position the timing cover on the front of the engine and refit the retaining bolts, finger tight only at this stage (photos). **Note:** *Where gear-driven timing components are employed, the fuel injection pump intermediate mounting flange retaining bolts also secure the timing cover.*

5   Lubricate the oil seal in the front of the timing cover and then slide the crankshaft pulley onto the front of the crankshaft (photo).

6   Now fully tighten the timing cover retaining bolts, progressively and in a diagonal sequence to avoid distortion.

7   Clean the pulley bolt of old sealer then apply thread-locking compound to the threads and fit the bolt and washer. Lock the flywheel ring gear (see photo 45.3B) to prevent the crankshaft from turning, then tighten the pulley bolt to the specified torque setting (photo).

48   Cylinder head – reassembly

1   With the cylinder head on its side, lubricate the valve stems and refit the valves to their correct guides.

2   Refit the lower valve spring retainer and then slide on the valve stem oil seal (photos).

3   Position the inner and outer valve springs and upper spring retainer over the valve stem (photos).

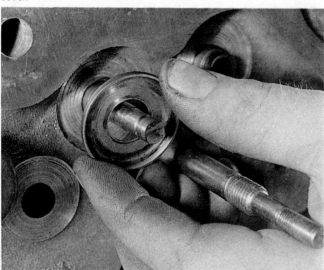

48.2A Fit the spring lower retainer ...

48.2B ... and valve stem oil seal

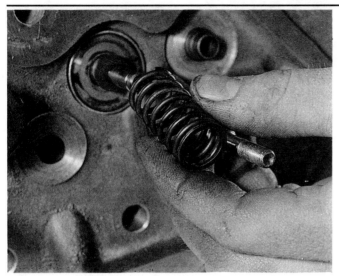

48.3A fit the inner spring ...

48.3B ... and outer spring ...

48.3C ... then the upper retainer

48.4 Compress the spring and fit the collets

4   Using a valve spring compressor, compress the springs and then refit the split collets (photo). A trace of grease will help to hold them in position on the valve stem until the spring compressor is released.

5   Release the valve spring compressor and check that the collets are correctly in position. Give the top of the valve stem a few taps with a soft-faced mallet to fully settle the collets and springs.

6   The cylinder head ancillary items (as listed in Section 15) can either be fitted at this stage or left until after the cylinder head is refitted to the engine. The manifolds, however, should only be refitted once the cylinder head is in place.

49   Cylinder head – refitting (engine out of car)

1   The next step is to thoroughly clean the faces of the block and cylinder head to remove all traces of old cylinder head gasket or jointing compound. Clean out the retaining bolt holes with a piece of wire and rag. Run the bolts up and down to make sure that they are all free and that the threads are clean. Finally wipe over the block and cylinder head faces with a petrol-moistened rag.

2   On 2.1 litre engines, remove the liner retaining clamps.

3   On 2.3 and 2.5 litre engines, the cylinder head gasket is selected for thickness in accordance with the piston protrusion above the cylinder block mating face (when at the top of the stroke). The gaskets are marked for thickness in accordance with the number of notches in the tab section at the rear edge of the gasket (photo). If the original cylinder block, pistons and cylinder head are being used, the replacement gasket must be of the same thickness as that removed, but if in doubt or if any of the previously mentioned engine components have been removed, check the piston protrusion to assess the gasket requirement. To do this, set the crankshaft at the TDC position, then use a dial gauge to measure the amount of piston protrusion and select the appropriate gasket as specified.

4   Certain modifications have been made to the cylinder head of the 2.3 and 2.5 litre engine models and these must be considered to ensure correct reassembly:

(a)   *The cylinder head retaining bolts were modified and later cylinder heads have stiffening ribs (Fig. 1.16). Later bolts have thread lengths of 70 and 95 mm and have KL and KSL identification marks on their heads. Earlier bolts have 33 mm long threads and are marked KC on their heads*

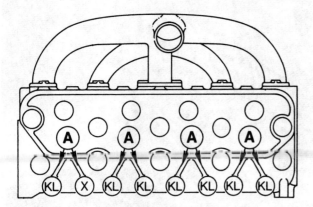

Fig. 1.16 Late type cylinder head showing stiffening ribs (A) and KL bolts fitted in place of the KC type used previously (Sec 49)

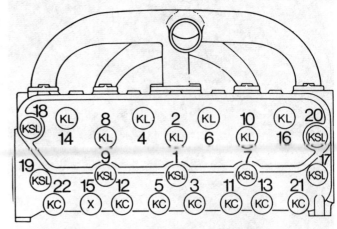

Fig. 1.17 Cylinder head bolt positions and tightening sequence – 2.1 litre engine (Sec 49)

KC	Short bolts	KSL	Long bolts
KL	Medium length bolts	X	Stud

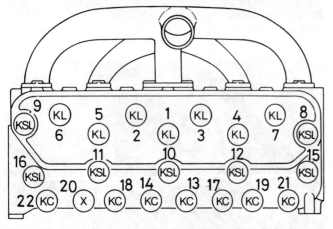

Fig. 1.18 Cylinder head bolt positions and tightening sequence – 2.3 and 2.5 litre engines (Sec 49)

KC	Short bolts	X	Stud
KL	Medium length bolts		KC type bolts replaced by
KSL	Long bolts		more KL types from
			engine no. FD 23314

49.3 Cylinder head gasket thickness identification marks (2.3 and 2.5 litre engines)

(b) *A later type cylinder head gasket is fitted and this is identified by a red seal band on its mating faces. Check with your Ford dealer before fitting this gasket type to earlier engines with clamped type injectors – it may not be permissible*

(c) *If an earlier type cylinder head gasket is being fitted, the early (KC) or late (KL and KSL) bolts can be used but do ensure that the bolts are tightened to the later torque wrench setting specified*

5   Place the cylinder head gasket in position on the top face of the block with the larger crimped area toward the block face (photo). Do not use any jointing compound on the gasket unless advised to do so on the gasket manufacturer's instructions.

6   Carefully lower the cylinder head onto the cylinder block (photo).

7   Insert all the retaining bolts and plain washers, noting the three different lengths. Also locate the single stud bolt (photo).

8   The bolts must now be tightened using the sequence shown in Fig. 1.17 or 1.18. Tighten each bolt in turn to the Stage 1 torque setting, then further tighten to the Stage 2 setting. Loosen off all bolts (in sequence) by 90°, then retighten them (in sequence) to the Stage 3 setting. The Stage 4 and 5 settings are completed after the engine is restarted and differ according to model (and cylinder head bolt type on 2.3 and 2.5 litre models). Refer to the torque settings in the Specifications (photo).

49.5 Fit the cylinder head gasket (2.3 litre shown)

49.6 Lowering the cylinder head into position (2.3 litre shown)

49.7 Fit the cylinder head bolts. Note location of the stud bolt (arrowed) – 2.3 litre shown

49.8 Tighten the cylinder head bolts to the specified torque setting

49.10 Insert the pushrods (2.3 litre shown)

49.11A Fit the rubber seal and washer to the rocker gear lubrication collar ...

49.11B ... fit the rocker gear assembly ...

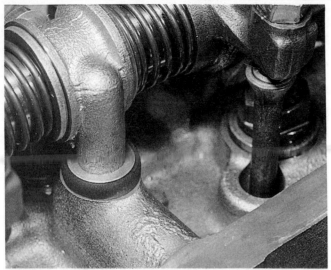

49.11C ... engaging the lubrication collar ...

49.11D ... then fit the washers and retaining nuts

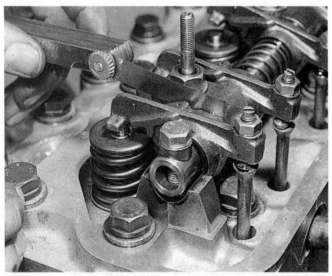

49.11E Check the rocker arm to pedestal clearance is as specified ...

49.11F ... then tighten retaining nuts to the specified torque

49.13A Refit the front ...

49.13B ... and rear tappet side covers

49.14A Fit the rocker gear oil feed pipe ...

49.14B ... the exhaust manifold ...

49.14C ... and inlet manifold (2.3 litre shown)

9 On the 2.1 litre engine, lubricate the tappets and fit them into their respective bores in the cylinder block (via the side access cover apertures).

10 On all engines, insert the pushrods into the appropriate tappet port from which each were removed (photo). Ensure that the end of each pushrod fully engages with its tappet.

11 Fit the rubber seal and washer to the locating peg of the lubrication collar on the rocker gear unit, then carefully lower the rocker shaft assembly onto the studs of the cylinder head. Ensure that the lubrication collar in the centre of the shaft seats correctly into its oil feed hole, with a new seal fitted (photos). Before tightening the rocker assembly fully into position, check that a clearance of 0.1 mm (0.004 in) exists between the rocker levers and the end pedestals.

12 Secure the rocker shaft assembly with the nuts and end post retaining bolts. As the nuts and bolts are tightened, make sure that the ball end of each rocker arm is sitting snugly in the pushrod cup, and is not trapped or dislodged to one side. Tighten the rocker shaft assembly to the specified torque wrench setting.

13 If still to be fitted, locate the tappet side covers with new gaskets to the side of the cylinder block (photos). When fitting the rear cover, remember that the oil pipe location clip is secured by the top rear cover

bolt. The rocker gear oil feed pipe and the oil filter-to-brake vacuum pump pipe (or turbo unit, as applicable) are both secured by this clip and the latter pipe is also secured at the rear of the cylinder head by a clip attached to the coolant end cover retaining bolt. Both pipes can be located in their clips at this stage, but leave fully tightening the clip bolts until after the pipes have been fitted to their connections at each end. When fitting the rocker gear oil supply pipe, use new copper washers on each side of the banjo unions.

14 Refit the inlet and exhaust manifolds. Note that the inlet manifold is not fitted with a gasket on normally aspirated models (photos).

15 Adjust the valve clearances as described in Section 51.

50 Cylinder head – refitting (engine in car)

1 Proceed as described in the previous Section to fit the cylinder head to the engine, then refer to Section 7 and reconnect the associated items to the cylinder head in the reverse order of removal.

2 Refer to Chapter 2 for details concerning refitting of the radiator and to top up the cooling system.

3 Refer to Chapter 3 for details concerning the fuel system components.

4 When the engine is restarted, check for any signs of leaks from the oil, fuel and cooling system attachments to the cylinder head.

5 When the engine has warmed up to its normal operating temperature, run it at 3000 rpm for a period of ten minutes then switch it off and allow it to cool over a period of four hours, then remove the rocker cover and tighten the head bolts to the Stage 4 and, where applicable, Stage 5 torque settings (see Specifications).

6 Recheck and adjust the valve clearances, then refit the rocker cover.

51 Valve clearances – adjustment

1 The valve adjustments should be made with the engine cold. The importance of correct rocker arm/valve stem clearances cannot be overstressed as they vitally affect the performance of the engine. If the

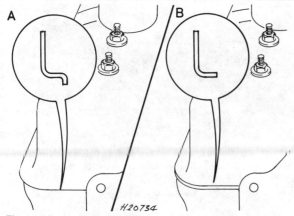

Fig. 1.19 Early (A) and late (B) type rocker covers with insets
showing mating face profiles (Sec 51)

clearances are set too open, the efficiency of the engine is reduced as
the valves open late and close earlier than was intended. If, on the other
hand, the clearances are set too close there is a danger that the valve
stems will expand upon heating or not allow the valves to close
properly, which will cause burning of the valve head and seat, and
possibly warping. If the engine is in the car, access to the rockers is
gained by removing the rocker cover.

2   It should be noted that the two types of rocker cover have been
fitted to the 2.3 and 2.5 litre models (Fig. 1.19). When removing the later
type rocker cover, particular care must be taken not to damage the
cover gasket or to allow it to become unstuck from the cover – in either
case it will need renewal. If renewal of the silicone type gasket is
necessary, ensure that the mating surfaces are clean, then smear the
cover mating surface with a 2 mm wide bead of sealant adhesive
(supplied with the rocker cover/cylinder head gasket set) and locate the
gasket to the rocker cover. The adhesive must be allowed fully to dry
(for about 45 minutes) before refitting the rocker cover. This should be
taken into account before final refitting of the rocker cover after final
tightening of the cylinder head bolts and/or adjusting the valve clearances, since application of the adhesive at this stage will save time later.

3   It is important that the valve clearances are set when the tappet of
the valve being adjusted is on the heel of the cam (ie opposite the peak).

4   Turn the engine over by hand in its normal direction of rotation to
the point where the No 1 cylinder valves are overlapping. This is
indicated by the inlet and exhaust rocker arms/pushrods of that cylinder
each moving in opposing directions. Remember that the No 1 cylinder is
at the flywheel end. The inlet and exhaust valves of the No 4 cylinder
(radiator end) can now be checked for clearance and if required, adjusted to the specified clearance. Use a feeler gauge of the specified
thickness to check the clearance between the valve and the rocker arm
(photo). The gauge blade should be a light interference fit between the
two. If adjustment is necessary, loosen off the adjuster locknut with a
spanner, turn the adjuster screw to set the clearance, then holding it in
this position, retighten the locknut. Recheck the adjustment before
moving on to the next valve. The adjuster screw sometimes moves a
fraction when the locknut is being tightened and in this instance further
minor adjustment may be needed.

5   With the No 4 cylinder inlet and exhaust valve clearances adjusted,
continue turning the crankshaft in its normal direction to the point
where the No 3 cylinder valves are overlapping, then check/adjust the
No 2 cylinder valves in the same manner.

6   When the No 2 cylinder valves are adjusted, turn the crankshaft
further to the point where the No 4 cylinder valves are overlapping, then
check/adjust the No 1 cylinder valves.

7   Finally, with the No 1 cylinder valve clearances set correctly, turn
the crankshaft to the point where the No 2 valves are overlapping and
then check/adjust the No 3 cylinder valves.

8   When the valve clearances have all been set, the rocker cover can be

51.4 Adjusting the valve clearances

refitted, unless the cylinder head retaining bolts have yet to be finally
tightened and/or the valve timing is to be checked. When fitting the
cover, ensure that the mating surfaces are clean, and when fitting a
cover with a silicone gasket, lightly smear the mating surface on the
cylinder head with clean oil prior to assembly. Tighten the cover
retaining nuts or bolts (as applicable) to the specified torque wrench
setting.

52   Ancillary components – refitting

1   This is a reversal of the removal sequence given in Section 13 in this
Chapter.

2   Always use new gaskets when refitting previously removed components, and refer to the appropriate Chapter of this manual for the full
installation instructions for the component concerned.

3   Depending on model, leave fitting of the alternator, water pump and
power steering pump units until after the engine is refitted.

4   If the engine and transmission are being refitted together, refit the
starter motor at this stage. With long body starter motors, the engine
support arm can be fitted to the left-hand side of the cylinder block prior
to fitting.

53   Engine only – refitting

1   The refitting sequence is in general a reversal of the removal
procedure, but the following additional notes should be of assistance.

2   With the engine suitably suspended over the engine compartment,
carefully lower it until the centre of the flywheel/clutch unit is in line with
the transmission input shaft. As the engine is lowered, manoeuvre the
clutch cable over the protruding part of the sump side section. When the
engine is in-line with the transmission and the input shaft, move the
engine rearwards and engage it with the clutch housing dowels, then
insert the retaining bolts. It may be necessary to turn the engine
crankshaft over slowly by hand by means of the front pulley to allow the
splines of the input shaft and the clutch disc to align with each other.

3   Refit the starter motor before refitting the engine mounting arm on
the left-hand side and where applicable, attach the engine earth lead to
the starter motor retaining bolt.

4   Tighten the engine-to-transmission bolts and the engine mounting bolts to the specified torque settings.

5   Refit the alternator, water pump drivebelt tensioner pulley and where applicable, the power steering pump unit and the brake vacuum unit. Refer to the appropriate Chapter for details and adjust the tension of the drivebelts.

6   Refer to Chapter 3 and connect the fuel system components.

7   Refer to Chapter 2 for details on refitting the cooling system components, then refill the cooling system.

8   Ensure that all wiring connections are correctly and securely made.

9   Secure the engine crossmember and, if the brake lines attached to it were detached, reconnect them and top up the brake hydraulic fluid reservoir and bleed the brake system as described in Chapter 5.

10   Check that the sump drain plug is securely fitted, then top up the engine oil level with the correct grade and quantity of engine oil.

11   Leave refitting the engine undertray (where applicable) until after the engine had been restarted and the relevant oil, coolant and fuel system leakage checks have been made.

54   Engine and transmission – refitting

1   The sequence for refitting is basically the reverse to that of removal and should present no particular problems. The following additional points should be noted.

2   As the transmission will be attached to the engine before refitting, it will be necessary to lower the unit into the engine compartment at a steep angle. Assuming the car to be jacked up and supported on axle stands, or over a pit or hoist as in the removal operation, it may be necessary to support the engine on jacks when it is in position in the engine compartment and change the position of the lifting gear. This will make the final positioning of the power unit easier as it will not be at such a steep angle.

3   When the engine/transmission is in position, proceed as described in paragraphs 3 to 11 inclusive for general notes on reconnecting the engine.

4   Refer to the appropriate Chapter in this manual or the petrol engine manual (Book No 481, 903 or 1245, as applicable) for the model concerned and reconnect the transmission, propeller shaft and clutch cable.

5   Top up the transmission oil level to within 5 mm of the base of the oil level/filler plug in the side of the transmission housing and refit the plug.

6   As with the engine, do not refit the undertray until after the engine has been restarted and preferably after a test run, to ensure that all gears and the clutch engage/disengage in satisfactory manner. Also check that there are no oil leaks from the transmission.

55   Engine – initial start-up after major overhaul or repair

1   With the engine refitted to the car, make a visual check to see that everything has been reconnected and that no loose rags or tools have been left within the engine compartment.

2   Make sure that the battery is fully charged and that all coolant and lubricants are fully replenished. Prime the fuel system as described in Chapter 3.

3   The engine should start after the fuel priming operation.

4   As the engine fires and runs keep it going at a fast idle only (no faster) and allow it to reach normal working temperature.

5   As the engine warms up there will be odd smells and some smoke from parts getting hot and burning off oil deposits. The signs to look for are leaks of water or oil, which will be obvious if serious. Check also the exhaust pipe and manifold connections as these do not always find their exact gas tight position until the heat and vibration have acted on them – it is almost certain that they will need tightening further. This should be done, of course, with the engine stopped.

6   When normal operating temperature has been reached, stop the engine, and adjust the engine idle speed as described in Chapter 3.

7   Stop the engine and wait a few minutes to see if any coolant or lubricant is dripping out when the engine is stationary.

8   If the cylinder head was removed, it must be further tightened down to the Stage 4 (and Stage 5 where applicable) torque wrench settings. With the engine at its normal operating temperature, start and run it at 3000 rpm for a period of ten minutes, then stop the engine and allow it to cool down over a period of four hours. When completely cooled off, remove the rocker cover and tighten the cylinder head bolts to the Stage four and, where applicable, Stage 5 torque wrench settings (see Specifications).

9   Recheck and adjust the valve clearances (Section 51), then refit the rocker cover (see paragraph 2 in Section 51).

10   Road test the car to check that the engine is giving the necessary smoothness and power. Do not race the engine – if new bearings and/or pistons have been fitted it should be treated as a new engine and run in at a reduced speed for the first 1000 miles (1600 km).

56   Compression test – description and interpretation

1   A compression test involves measuring the pressure developed in each cylinder when the engine is being cranked by the starter motor. It can be a valuable aid in fault diagnosis. A special compression tester will be needed, with an adaptor to connect it to a glow plug hole. Rather than buy such a tester it may be cheaper to let a Ford dealer or other specialist do the test.

2   The engine must be at normal operating temperature, the battery well charged and the valve clearances correct.

3   Disconnect the glow plug relay, then remove the glow plug bus bar and the glow plugs themselves. Refer to Chapter 3, Section 10 if necessary.

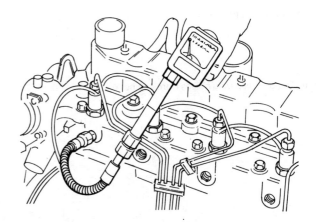

Fig. 1.20 Compression tester screwed into a glow plug hole (Sec 56)

4   Disconnect the fuel injection pump stop solenoid.

5   Screw the compression tester adaptor into one of the glow plug holes. Crank the engine on the starter and record the maximum pressure indicated on the tester.

6   Repeat the operations on the other three cylinders and record the pressures developed.

7   Compare the pressures with those given in the Specifications. Absolute values are not so significant as variation between cylinders.

8   A low reading in one cylinder may be due to burnt or poorly seating valves, to piston/bore wear, to a blown head gasket or a cracked head.

With petrol engines it is normal to introduce a teaspoon of oil into a low-reading cylinder: if this improves the compression temporarily, worn pistons or bores are indicated. Be wary of using this diagnostic aid on a Diesel engine, since there is much less combustion chamber space at TDC and a hydraulic lock may be caused.

9   A low reading obtained for two adjacent cylinders suggests strongly that the head gasket has blown between them.

10   Further tests (eg leakdown and cooling system pressure tests) may be needed to determine the likely causes of poor compression.

11   When the tests are complete, refit and reconnect the glow plugs, glow plug relay and stop solenoid.

---

57 Fault diagnosis – engine

Symptom	Reason(s)
Engine will not turn over when attempting to start	Battery discharged Loose battery connections Faulty starter motor or solenoid Earth strap broken or disconnected Fault in starting circuit wiring
Engine turns over but will not start, and emits black smoke	Fuel injection pump timing incorrect Fuel injectors faulty Lack of engine compression Obstruction in air intake system
Engine rotates but will not start, and emits white smoke	Cylinder head gasket leaking Cylinder head, cylinder block or liners (where applicable) cracked
Engine rotates but will not start, with no smoke emission	Fuel tank empty Air in fuel system Leak in fuel liner or unions Heater plugs inoperative Stop control jammed in stop position Fuel injection pump faulty Fuel injection faulty
Engine lacks power	Air intake system choked Fuel injection timing incorrect Fuel filter blocked Defective fuel injector Engine worn internally
Low oil pressure	Oil level too low Oil pressure warning light transmitter faulty Faulty or worn oil pump Oil pressure relief valve sticking Engine bearings and internal components worn
Thumping noises from engine	Fuel injector faulty Fuel injection pump timing incorrect Air in fuel system or leaks in fuel lines Incorrect valve timing Broken internal component
Whistling or whispering noises from engine	Defective cylinder head gasket Leak at heater plug Leak at fuel injector seating Poor seating of inlet on exhaust valves Leak at manifold joint faces

Chapter 2 Cooling system

Contents

Specifications

General .... Water-based coolant, pressurized system, assisted by pump and fan

Radiator.. Corrugated, fin-on-tube with plastic top/bottom or end tanks

Coolant
Type/specification.. Soft water, and antifreeze to Ford spec SSM- 97B 9103-A (Duckhams Universal Antifreeze and Summer Coolant)

Capacity:
  2.1 litre engine .... 10 litres (17.6 pints)
  2.3 litre engine .... 9.5 litres (16.7 pints)
  2.5 litre engine .... 11 litres (19.4 pints)
Recommended concentration of antifreeze.. 50% by volume

Filler cap pressure
2.1 and 2.5 litre (STP) engines .... 0.85 to 1.10 bar (12.3 to 16.0 lbf/in^2)
2.3 and 2.5 litre (STR and SFA) engines... 1.0 to 1.25 bar (14.5 to 18.1 lbf/in^2)

Water pump type .... Centrifugal

Thermostat
Type... Wax
Nominal rating:
  2.1 and 2.5 litre (STP) engines .... 72°C (162°F)
  2.3 and 2.5 litre (STR and SFA) engines .... 81°C (178°F)
Opening temperature (all models) .... 69° to 72°C (156° to 162°F)

Radiator fan
Type... Electro-magnetic or viscous coupling, depending on model
Fan to hub coupling air gap:
  2.1 litre engine .... 10 to 13 mm (0.4 to 0.5 in)
  2.3 litre engine .... 0.5 mm (0.02 in)
  2.5 litre .... 0.35 to 0.4 mm (0.014 to 0.016 in)

Drivebelts
Free play measured at midway point of longest span under finger
pressure .... 10 to 13 mm (0.39 to 0.51 in)

Torque wrench settings

2.1 and 2.5 litre (STP) engines	Nm	lbf ft
Radiator to front panel bolts..	8 to 11	6 to 8
Fan shroud to radiator bolts...	8 to 11	6 to 8
Water pump bolts	9 to 13	7 to 9.5
Water pump pulley nut..	30 to 40	22 to 29
Fan clutch nut...	7.0 to 7.5	5.2 to 5.5
Fan-to-fan clutch nut	8 to 10	6 to 7.4
2.3 and 2.5 litre (STR and SFA) engines – where different to above settings		
Fan clutch nut (2.3 and 2.5 litre)...	30 to 40	22 to 29
Alternator adjuster arm to timing cover (2.3 litre)	21 to 25	15 to 18
Water pump drivebelt adjuster (2.3 litre)	21 to 25	15 to 18
Water pump adjuster bolt (2.3 litre)...	21 to 25	15 to 18

1 General description

The cooling system is of pressurised type and includes a front mounted crossflow radiator, belt driven water pump, temperature conscious, electro-magnetic or viscous-coupled fan, wax type thermostat, and an expansion (degas) tank. The radiator is of corrugated fin-on-tube structure and the end tanks are plastic.

The thermostat is located behind the water outlet elbow at the front of the cylinder head, and its purpose is to ensure rapid engine warm-up by restricting the flow of coolant in the engine when cold, and also to assist in regulating the normal operating temperature of the engine.

The expansion tank incorporates a pressure cap which effectively pressurises the cooling system as the coolant temperature rises thereby increasing the boiling point temperature of the coolant. The tank also

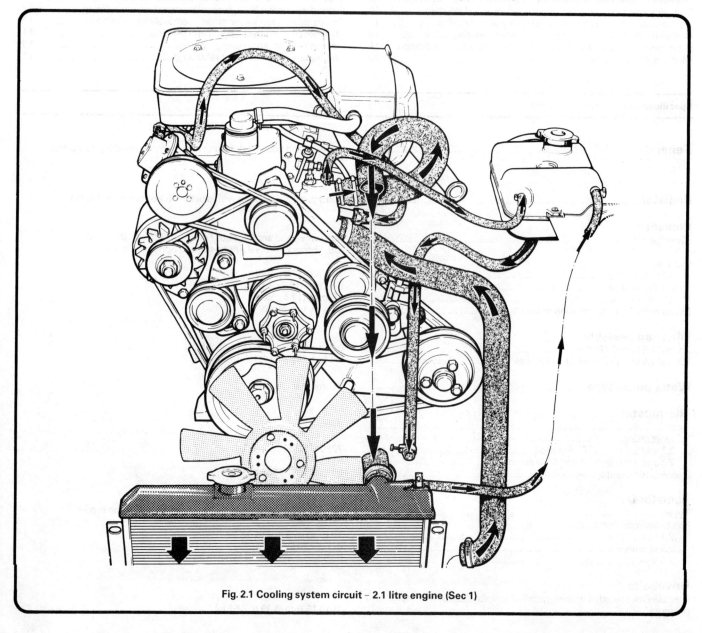

Fig. 2.1 Cooling system circuit – 2.1 litre engine (Sec 1)

has a further degas function. Any accumulation of air bubbles in the coolant, in particular in the thermostat housing and the radiator, is returned to the tank and released in the air space thus maintaining the efficiency of the coolant.

The radiator is provided with a drain plug and drain plugs are also provided on each side of the cylinder block.

The system functions as follows. Cold water in the bottom of the radiator circulates through the bottom hose to the water pump where the pump impeller pushes the water through the passages within the cylinder block and cylinder head. After cooling the cylinder bores, combustion surfaces, and valve seats, the water reaches the underside of the thermostat which is initially closed. A small proportion of water passes through the small hose from the thermostat housing to the expansion tank, but because the thermostat is closed the main circulation is through the heater matrix, returning to the water pump. When the coolant reaches the predetermined temperature the thermostat opens and hot water passes through the top hose to the top of the radiator. As the water circulates down through the radiator, it is cooled by the passage of air past the radiator when the car is in forward motion, supplemented by the action of the fan as necessary. Having reached the bottom of the radiator, the water is now cooled and the cycle is repeated. Circulation of water continues through the expansion tank, and heater at all times, the heater temperature control being by an air flap.

Vehicles operating in severe climatic or operating conditions may be fitted with a secondary cooling fan which is thermo-electrically operated and is located in front of the radiator.

Turbo models are fitted with an air-cooled oil cooler unit which is mounted just forward of the base of the radiator. The oil cooler on other models is a water-cooled unit and is located between the engine oil filter and its mounting.

2 Routine maintenance

1   Weekly, every 250 miles (400 km) or before a long journey, check the coolant level by inspecting the expansion tank. The tank is translucent, so the level can be verified without removing the cap. The level should be between the MAX and MIN marks; if it is below the MIN mark, proceed as follows.

2   **Take great care to avoid scalding if the system is hot.** Place a thick cloth over the expansion tank cap and turn the cap anti-clockwise as far as the first stop. Wait for any steam to be released, then depress the cap, turn it further anti-clockwise and remove it completely.

3   Top up to the MAX mark using antifreeze mixture of the correct type and concentration – see Section 7. In an emergency plain water

may be used, but this will dilute the antifreeze remaining in the system. Do not add cold water to an overheated engine, or damage may result.

4   Refit the expansion tank cap when the level is correct. Check for leaks if frequent topping-up is required. Normally loss from this type of system is minimal.

5   At every major service interval, inspect all coolant hoses and hose clips for security and good condition. Renew damaged or defective hoses without delay.

6   At alternate major service intervals, check the condition and tension of the drivebelts. Refer to Section 8 for details.

7   Every two years or 36 000 miles (60 000 km), drain the cooling system, flush it if necessary and refill with new coolant. Refer to Sections 4, 5, 6 and 7. At the same time consider renewing the coolant hoses and the water pump/alternator drivebelt on a preventive basis.

8   It is prudent to check the antifreeze concentration at the beginning of winter if the coolant is not due for renewal. Checking is done using a special hydrometer which is possessed by most garages.

3 Pressure test – description and interpretation

1   In cases where leakage is difficult to trace, or some other malfunction of the cooling system is suspected, a pressure test can prove helpful. The test involves pressurising the system by means of a hand pump and an adaptor which is fitted to the expansion tank in place of the filler cap. The resourceful home mechanic may be able to improvise something from (eg) a spare filler cap and tyre inflation equipment; alternatively, the test can be performed by a Ford dealer or most other garages.

2   Bring the engine to normal operating temperature, then switch it off.

3   Place a thick cloth over the expansion tank cap. Turn the cap anti-clockwise to the first stop and wait for any pressure to be released. Depress the cap and turn it further anti-clockwise to remove it. Take care to avoid scalding.

4   Connect the pressure test equipment to the expansion tank filler hole. Apply the specified test pressure and check that it is held for at least ten seconds. If the pressure drops within ten seconds, check for leaks. Release the pressure and disconnect the equipment.

5   Besides leaks from hoses, pressure can also be lost through leaks in the radiator and heater matrix. A blown head gasket, or a bracket head or block, can give rise to "invisible" leakage. Usually there are other clues to this condition, such as coolant contamination of the oil or combustion gases entering the coolant.

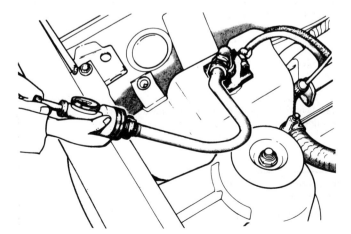

Fig. 2.2 Typical cooling system test method (Sec 3)

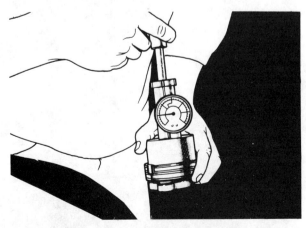

Fig. 2.3 Testing the blow-off pressure of the expansion tank cap
(Sec 3)

4.5A Loosening off the radiator drain plug (2.3 litre engine)

4.5B Detaching the radiator bottom hose

6   The condition of the filler/pressure relief valve cap must not be overlooked. Normally, it is tested with similar equipment to that used for the pressure test. The blow-off pressure is given in the Specifications, and is also usually stamped on the cap. Renew the cap if it will not hold the specified pressure, or if its condition is otherwise doubtful.

5   On 2.3 and 2.5 litre models, a drain plug is fitted to the radiator and is located on the left-hand side of the bottom tank in the front or rear face (depending on model). Loosen off the drain plug and allow the coolant to drain into a suitable container. If the bottom hose is lower than the drain plug, detach the hose and allow the coolant to drain from it (photos).

6   An engine drain plug is fitted on each side of the cylinder block (towards the rear). Unscrew and remove these plugs to allow full drainage of coolant from the engine.

4   Cooling system – draining

1   It is preferable to drain the cooling system with the engine cold. If this is not possible, place a thick cloth over the expansion tank filler cap and turn it slowly 90° in an anti-clockwise direction until the first step is reached, then wait until all the pressure has been released. Be prepared for the emission of very hot steam, as the release of pressure may cause the coolant to boil.

2   Remove the filler cap.

3   Detach and remove the engine undertray.

4   On 2.1 litre models, loosen off the clip and detach the bottom hose from the radiator and drain the coolant into a suitable container.

5   Cooling system – flushing

1   After some time the radiator and engine waterways may become restricted or even blocked with scale or sediment, which reduces the efficiency of the cooling system. When this occurs, the coolant will appear rusty and dark in colour and the system should then be flushed. Begin by draining the cooling system as described in Section 4.

2   Disconnect the top hose from the radiator (photo), then insert a hose and allow water to circulate through the radiator until it runs clear from the outlet.

3   Insert the hose in the expansion tank filler neck and allow water to run out of the cylinder block and bottom hose until clear.

4   In severe cases of contamination, the system should be reverse flushed. To do this, remove the radiator, insert it, and insert a hose in the outlet. Continue flushing until clear water runs from the inlet.

5   The engine should also be reverse flushed. To do this, remove the thermostat and insert the hose into the cylinder head. Continue flushing until clear water runs from the cylinder block drain plug and bottom hose.

6   The use of chemical cleaners should only be necessary as a last resort, and the regular renewal of the antifreeze/corrosion inhibitor solution should prevent the contamination of the system.

6   Cooling system – filling

1   Refit the radiator and thermostat.

2   Reconnect the hose(s) then refit and tighten the cylinder block drain plugs. Check that the radiator drain plug is securely tightened.

5.2 Detaching the radiator top hose

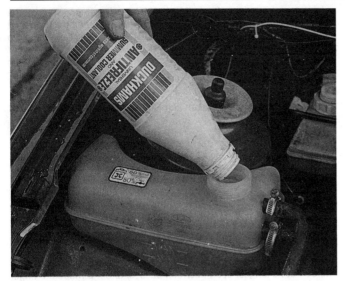

6.3A Topping-up the cooling system (2.3 litre engine)

6.3B Topping-up the cooling system (Turbo engine)

3   Pour coolant into the expansion tank filler neck until it reaches the maximum level mark, then refit the cap (photos).

4   Run the engine at a fast idling speed for several minutes, then stop the engine and check the level in the expansion tank. Top up the level as necessary, being careful to release pressure from the system before removing the filler cap.

5   Check the system hoses and connections for any sign of leaks, then refit the engine undertray.

7 Antifreeze/corrosion inhibitor mixture general

Note: *The antifreeze/corrosion inhibitor mixture is toxic and must not be allowed to contact the skin. Precautions must also be taken to prevent the mixture contacting the bodywork and clothing.*

1   The antifreeze/corrosion inhibitor should be renewed every two years or 36 000 miles (60 000 km) whichever comes first. This is necessary not only to maintain the antifreeze properties (although the antifreeze content does not deteriorate), but mostly to prevent corrosion which would otherwise occur as the properties of the inhibitors become progressively less effective.

2   Always use the antifreeze recommended in the Specifications and by the manufacturers.

3   Before adding the mixture, the cooling system should be completely drained and flushed, and all hose connections checked for tightness.

4   The mixture consists of 50% antifreeze and 50% water. Mix the required quantity in a clean container then fill the cooling system with reference to Section 5.

5   After filling, a label should be attached to the radiator stating the type of antifreeze and the date installed. Any subsequent topping-up should be made with the same type and concentration of antifreeze.

8 Drivebelts – checking, renewal and adjustment

1   The condition of the drivebelts and their adjustment must be checked at the intervals given in the *Routine Maintenance* section at the start of this manual. Check the full length of the drivebelts for signs of cracks and general deterioration. The tension adjustment can

be checked by depressing each belt in turn at the midway point of the longest span between pulleys under a moderate finger pressure. Measure the amount of deflection and compare it with the specified requirement. If any of the drivebelts are in need of replacement of adjustment, proceed as described below according to belt and model.

2   The following points of caution should be noted when adjusting the tension of a drivebelt:

(a)   *Unless specified, do not use a lever bar to assist in pivoting the adjuster unit to take up the tension adjustment. Hand pressure should be sufficient*

(b)   *Never over-tension a drivebelt as this will reduce the life of both the belt and the component bearings*

2.1 litre engine
Brake vacuum pump drivebelt
3   To remove the drivebelt, loosen off the pump mounting bolts and pivot the pump in towards the engine to slacken off the belt tension,

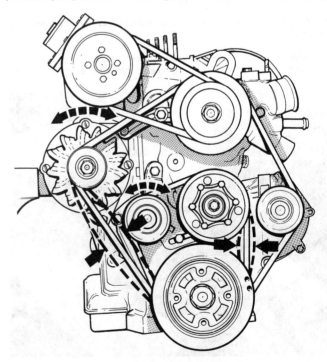

Fig. 2.4 Drivebelt tension check and adjustment points on the 2.1 litre engine (Sec 8)

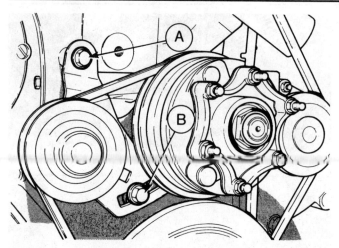

Fig. 2.5 Fan belt jockey wheel pivot bolt (A) and adjuster bolt (B) on the 2.1 litre engine (Sec 8)

then disengage the belt from the vacuum pump and water pump pulleys.

4   Refit the drivebelt in the reverse order of removal. Adjust the tension of the belt as follows.

5   With the vacuum pump retaining bolts hand tight, pivot the pump away from the engine to take up the belt tension to the point where the belt deflection under finger pressure at the midway point of the belt at its longest span between the pulleys is as specified. Tighten the pump mounting bolts to set the adjustment. When the engine has run for about fifteen minutes, stop it and recheck the tension of the drivebelt. Further minor adjustment may be required, particularly when a new belt has been fitted.

Alternator/water pump drivebelt
6   Remove the brake vacuum pump drivebelt as previously described.

7   Loosen off the alternator adjuster and mounting bolts, pivot the alternator inwards to slacken off the belt tension, then disengage the belt from the pulleys and remove it.

8   Refit in the reverse order of removal and adjust the belt tension as follows.

9   With the alternator mounting/adjustment bolts hand tight, pivot the alternator away from the engine to take up the belt tension to the point

where the deflection of the drivebelt under finger pressure at the midway point of the longest span is as specified. Tighten the mounting and adjuster bolts to set the adjustment. After the engine has been run for about fifteen minutes, stop it, recheck the belt tension. Further minor adjustment may be necessary, particularly if a new drivebelt has been fitted.

Cooling fan drivebelt
10   Remove the brake vacuum and alternator drivebelts as described previously.

11   Loosen off the jockey wheel pivot bolt and the adjuster bracket bolt (Fig. 2.5). Pivot the jockey wheel towards the fan hub and slacken the tension from the drivebelt sufficiently to enable it to be disengaged from the pulleys and removed.

12   Refit the drivebelt in the reverse order of removal. Adjust its tension as follows.

13   With the drivebelt jockey pulley pivot and adjuster bolts hand tight only, pivot the jockey pulley outwards away from the fan hub to take up the tension and provide the specific deflection at the midway point of the belt at its longest span between pulleys, under a moderate finger pressure. Tighten the adjuster and jockey retaining bolts to set the tension.

14   Recheck the tension of the belt after the engine has been run for a period of about fifteen minutes. Further minor adjustment may be required, particularly when a new belt has been fitted.

2.3 and 2.5 litre engines
Fan/PAS pump drivebelt
15   Loosen the adjuster bolt of the PAS pump, or the jockey pulley on non-power steering models. Pivot the pump or jockey pulley unit to loosen the belt tension and disengage the belt from the pulleys.

16   Refit in the reverse order of removal but adjust the belt tension as follows.

17   With the PAS or jockey pulley unit bolts loosened off, pivot the unit outwards to take up the belt tension and provide the specified deflection at the midway point of the longest span between pulleys under finger pressure. Tighten the adjuster unit mounting bolts to set the drivebelt tension. Recheck the tension after the engine has been run for a period of fifteen minutes. Further minor adjustment may be required, particularly when a new belt has been fitted (photos).

Brake vacuum pump drivebelt (2.3 litre)
18   Proceed as described for the same belt in paragraphs 3 to 5 for the

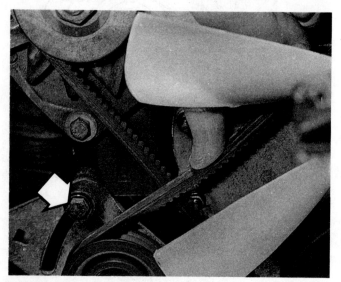

8.17A Cooling fan drivebelt adjustment check. The jockey pulley unit bolt (non-PAS models) is arrowed

8.17B PAS unit showing mounting and adjuster strap bolts (arrowed)

8.18 Brake vacuum pump drivebelt tension adjustment

8.20A Alternator and drivebelt

8.20B Alternator/drivebelt adjuster strap

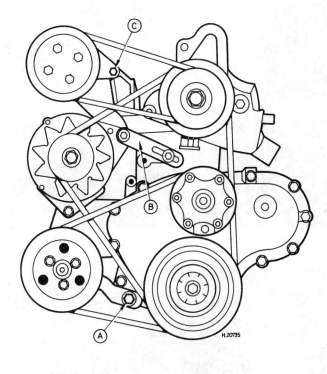

Fig. 2.6 Drivebelts layout – 2.3 litre engine (Sec 8)

A   Power steering pump   C   Vacuum pump pivot bolt
B   Alternator adjuster arm

2.1 litre engine model for replacement and tension adjustment. Later models are fitted with a pump/drivebelt adjuster bracket, in which case loosen off the pivot and adjuster bolts to allow adjustment of the drivebelt tension (photo).

Alternator/water pump drivebelt

19   Remove the cooling fan/PAS drivebelt as described previously.

20   Loosen off the alternator mounting and adjuster strap bolts, pivot

8.22 Alternator drivebelt tension adjustment check

the alternator inward to slacken the tension, then remove the drivebelt from the pulleys (photos).

21   Refit the drivebelt in the reverse order of removal. Adjust the belt tension as follows.

22   With the alternator mounting and adjuster strap bolts loosened off, pivot the alternator outwards from the engine to take up the belt tension and provide the specified deflection under finger pressure at the mid-way point of the longest belt span between pulleys. Tighten the adjuster and mounting bolts to set the tension. When the engine has been run for a period of about fifteen minutes, stop it and recheck the tension. Further minor adjustment may be required particularly when a new belt has been fitted (photo).

9   Radiator – removal and refitting

1   Raise and support the car at the front end on axle stands. The radiator on the Sierra and later Granada models is removed downwards from the vehicle, so allow for sufficient clearance underneath for removal.

2   Drain the engine coolant as described in Section 3.

3   Where applicable, detach and remove the engine undershield.

4   Detach the top, bottom and expansion (degas) tank hoses from the radiator. Also where applicable, detach the radiator bottom hose from the radiator/lower cowl (photos).

5   Where applicable, detach the sound insulation panels from the radiator/fan shroud.

6   On the 2.1 litre model, undo the four retaining bolts and move the fan cowl back from the radiator and locate it out of the way over the fan.

7   On 2.3 and 2.5 litre models, release the retaining bolts and clips, then separate the upper and lower fan shroud sections and remove them (photos).

8   Disconnect the lead from the temperature sensor on the radiator (photo). On 2.1 litre models, undo the four retaining bolts and then carefully withdraw the radiator from the car.

9   On 2.3 and 2.5 litre models, undo the two radiator retaining bolts then release the plastic retaining clip and washer each side (through the access apertures in the top crosspanel), then carefully disengage and withdraw the radiator downwards from the car (photos).

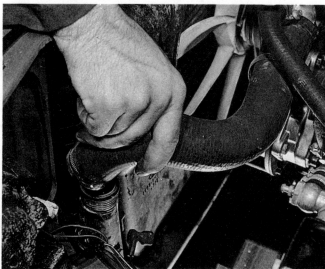

9.4A Detach the radiator top ...

9.4B ... and bottom hoses

9.4C Unbolt the bottom hose from the cowl ...

9.4D ... and release it from the retaining clip

9.7A Undo the retaining bolts and ...

9.7B ... extract the flange clips ...

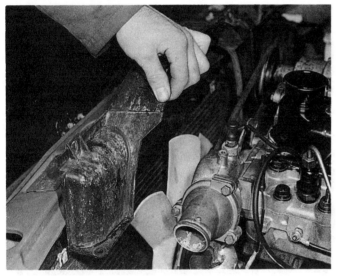

9.7C ... and remove the radiator upper cowl

9.7D Unscrew the retaining bolts (one arrowed) ...

9.7E ... and withdraw the radiator lower cowl

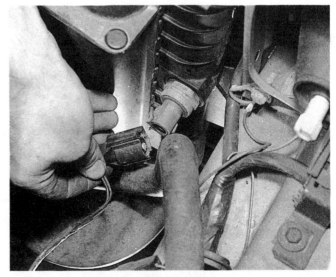

9.8 Disconnect the temperature sensor lead

9.9A Release the radiator retaining clips and ...

9.9B ... withdraw the washers ...

9.9C Unscrew the lower mounting bolt each side (one arrowed) ...

9.9D ... and lower the radiator to remove it

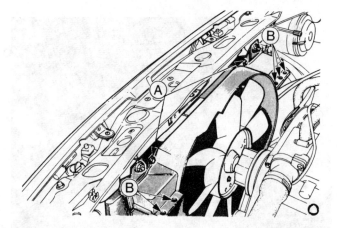

Fig. 2.7 Cooling fan shroud upper fixings on later 2.3 litre engines (Sec 9)

| A | Bolts (to radiator) | B | Clips (Upper to lower shroud) |

10   Refitting is a reversal of the removal procedure. Refill the cooling system as described in Section 6.

10   Radiator – inspection and repair

1   If the radiator has been removed because of suspected blockage, reverse-flush it as described in Section 4.

2   Clean dirt and debris from the radiator fins, using an air jet or water and a soft brush. Be careful not to damage the fins, or cut your fingers.

3   A radiator specialist can perform a 'flow test' on the radiator to establish whether an internal blockage exists.

4   A leaking radiator must be referred to a specialist for permanent repair. Do not attempt to weld or solder a leaking radiator, as damage to the plastic parts may result.

5   Temporary 'cold' repairs may be made using proprietary compounds sold for this purpose.

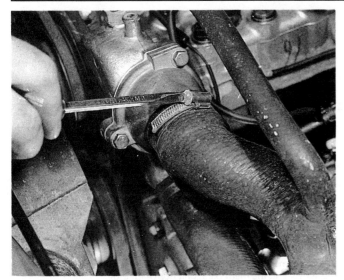

11.2A Detaching the top hose from the thermostat housing

11.2B Thermostat and housing removal (2.3 litre engine)

11   Thermostat – removal, testing and refitting

1   As it is not necessary to fully drain the cooling system to remove the thermostat housing, disconnect the bottom hose from the water pump housing and drain the coolant into a suitable container for re-use, but take care if the coolant is hot (see precautionary notes on coolant draining in Section 4).

2   Disconnect the expansion tank and top hoses from the thermostat housing at the front of the cylinder head and remove the three bolts securing the housing. Lift off the housing and thermostat (photos).

3   On 2.1 litre models, extract the thermostat unit from the top hose.

4   To test the thermostat suspend it with a piece of string in a container of water. Gradually heat the water and note the temperature at which the thermostat starts to open. Remove the thermostat from the water and check that it is fully closed when cold.

5   Renew the thermostat if the opening temperature is not as given in the Specifications or if the unit does not fully close when cold.

6   Clean the housing and the mating face of the cylinder head. Check the thermostat sealing ring for condition and renew it if necessary (photo).

7   Refitting is a reversal of the removal procedure. Ensure that the thermostat is correctly orientated as it is fitted and on the 2.1 litre model,

Fig. 2.8 Thermostat and seal ring. Note direction of flow arrow (Sec 11)

11.6 Removing the seal ring from the thermostat

Fig. 2.9 Method of checking thermostat opening temperature (Sec 11)

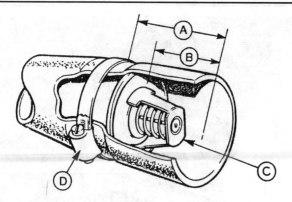

Fig. 2.10 Thermostat location in top hose – 2.1 litre engine (Sec 11)

A   35 mm (1.4 in)   C   Thermostat
B   25 mm (1.0 in)   D   Clip

insert the thermostat into position in the hose to the specified depth shown in Fig. 2.10.

8   On completion, refill the cooling system as described in Section 6 of this Chapter.

12 Water pump – removal and refitting

1   Drain the cooling system as described in Section 4.

2   On the 2.1 litre engine model, refer to Section 9 and remove the radiator.

3   Release the retaining clips and detach the coolant hoses from the water pump and thermostat housing. If the hoses or any of the retaining clips are in poor condition, they must be renewed during refitting.

4   Disconnect the lead from the coolant sensor in the water pump/thermostat housing. If the water pump is to be renewed, remove the sensor and the thermostat unit from it (photo).

12.4 Disconnecting the lead from the sensor in the housing

12.8A Withdraw the water pump pulley ...

12.8B ... and extract the Woodruff key

12.12A Refitting the water pump and new gasket (2.3 litre engine)

12.12B Locate the engine lift bracket on the upper retaining bolts

5   On 2.3 and 2.5 litre models, detach and remove the radiator upper shroud.
6   Before loosening off the tension of the water pump and associated drivebelts, increase the tension on the water pump drivebelt (by hand) and loosen off the nut retaining the water pump pulley. If the nut proves too tight and the pulley keeps turning, the pulley will need to be held with a suitable strap wrench after the drivebelt is removed, but take care not to damage the pulley.

7   Loosen off the relevant drive belt tension adjusters (according to model) and disengage the drivebelt from the water pump. Unless renewal is necessary, the drivebelt(s) need only be released to allow the water pump to be removed.

8   Unscrew and remove the water pump drive pulley retaining nut, withdraw the pulley and remove its Woodruff key from the shaft groove. Take care not to lose the key (photos).

9   Undo the five retaining bolts and remove the water pump from the cylinder head. As the bolts are removed, note the position of the engine lift bracket secured by the two upper bolts.

10   A leaky, noisy or otherwise defective pump must be renewed,

11   Clean the mating faces of the engine and the water pump before refitting.

12   Refitting is a reversal of the removal procedure, but use a new gasket. Refer to Section 11 for details on refitting the thermostat if this was removed (photos),

13   When refitting the temperature sensor unit, smear its threads lightly with sealant.

14   Refer to Section 8 for details on refitting and adjusting the tension of the drivebelt(s).

15   Refer to Section 9 for details on refitting the radiator on 2.1 litre models.

16   Refill the cooling system as described in Section 6.

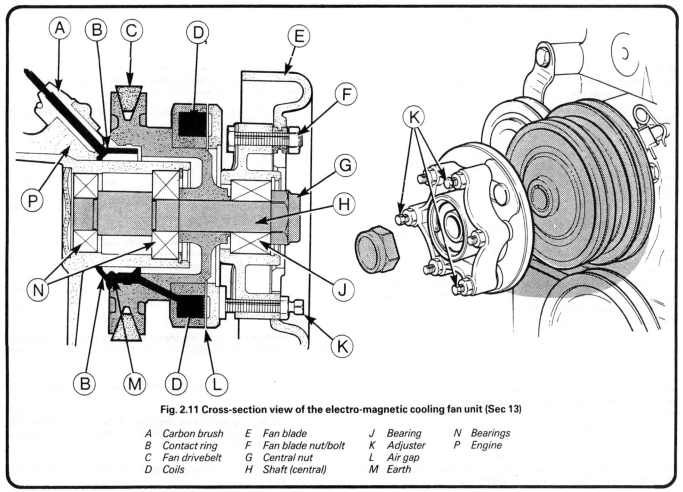

Fig. 2.11 Cross-section view of the electro-magnetic cooling fan unit (Sec 13)

A	Carbon brush	E	Fan blade	J	Bearing	N	Bearings
B	Contact ring	F	Fan blade nut/bolt	K	Adjuster	P	Engine
C	Fan drivebelt	G	Central nut	L	Air gap		
D	Coils	H	Shaft (central)	M	Earth		

13.3 Fan-to-hub retaining nuts (arrowed)

14.2 Electro-magnetic cooling fan pick-up brush (fan removed)

13 Electro-magnetic cooling fan – description and checking

1   This unit has two main parts, these being the electro-magnetic hub and the clutch unit. The electro-magnetic hub is engine driven by the fan drivebelt and is mounted directly onto the central shaft which in turn is mounted in the timing cover. The fan/clutch unit is also mounted on the central shaft by a ball-bearing which allows the fan to operate at an idle speed (independent of the belt drive), when the coolant temperature in the radiator bottom hose is below 71°C (160°F). As the coolant temperature rises above 85°C (185°F), the thermostatic control switch in the base of the radiator allows a flow of current between the contact ring and carbon brush to the fan hub coils. This causes a magnetic effect to pull the fan coupling clutch plate into contact with the pulley coupling and the fan speed is increased. When the coolant temperature drops, the current flow is interrupted, the diaphragm spring in the fan coupling pulls it back against the three stops and the fan then rotates at a normal idle speed under the influence of the air flow and the ball-bearing friction.

2   To operate efficiently, the fan drivebelt must obviously be in good condition and correctly adjusted as described in Section 8. The wiring connections between the coolant temperature sensor/switch and the electro-magnetic fan pick-up brush must be clean and secure. The carbon brush must be in good condition and the contact faces of the brush and the contact ring must be clean.

3   It is important that the air gap clearance between the fan hub coupling and the pulley hub is as specified. The engine must be cold when the gap is checked. To check the gap, first remove the fan from the hub by undoing the retaining nuts (photo). Insert a feeler gauge between the two contact faces and check that the clearance is as specified. Rotate the hub and make the check at several points around the contact face. If adjustment is necessary, loosen off the three adjuster bolt locknuts then turn the bolts as required to set the clearance as specified, then retighten the locknuts. Refit the fan.

14 Electro-magnetic cooling fan pick-up brush – renewal

1   Disconnect the battery earth (negative) lead.

2   Extract the brush retaining clip and withdraw the brush from its location housing in the top face of the timing case. Detach the lead connector and remove the brush and lead (photo).

3   Renew the brush if it is worn beyond an acceptable level.

4   Clean the contact faces of the brush and the contact ring with a petrol-moistened cloth. Clean any burnt or corroded areas on the contact ring using a suitable piece of glasspaper.

5   Refit in the reverse order of removal.

15 Electro-magnetic cooling fan clutch – removal and refitting

1   Drain the cooling system and remove the radiator as described previously in this Chapter.

2   Undo the three retaining bolts and withdraw the fan from the hub (see photo 13.3).

3   Remove the fan drivebelt as described in Section 8 of this Chapter.

4   Locate a suitable strap wrench into the groove of the fan drivebelt pulley to prevent it rotating, then unscrew the central hub nut.

5   Lightly tap the fan coupling with a hide mallet to withdraw the coupling from the shaft. Alternatively use a suitable puller to remove the coupling. Retrieve the Woodruff key from the shaft groove.

6   If the fan shaft and bearing are in need of renewal, remove the timing cover and replace the shaft and bearing as described in Section 6 of Chapter 1.

7   Refit in the reverse order of removal. Check the fan air gap coupling clearance as described in Section 13 in this Chapter before refitting the fan.

8   Refit the radiator and its associated components as described in Section 9 of this Chapter.

9   Refill the cooling system as described in Section 6, restart the engine and check for coolant leaks from the coolant hose connections before refitting the engine undertray.

10   Check for satisfactory operation of the cooling fan when the engine is warmed up.

Fig. 2.12 Secondary cooling fan removal with inset showing disengagement of hanging bracket from radiator flange (Sec 17)

16 Viscous cooling fan coupling – general

1 Some 2.3 and 2.5 litre models are fitted with a viscous coupling to drive the cooling fan, in place of the electro-magnetic type.

2 The removal and refitting procedure differs slightly from the electro-magnetic type, as follows.

3 The cooling fan and viscous coupling are removed as one unit. Unscrew the centre bolt (left-hand thread) and interlocking coupling securing the fan and coupling to the fan pulley. On some models it may be necessary to remove four bolts securing the fan and coupling to the pulley.

4 The viscous coupling is secured to the fan by four bolts. Note that the coupling is not serviceable and if faulty should be renewed as a complete unit.

5 Refitting is a reversal of removal.

17 Secondary cooling fan – description, removal and refitting

1 The secondary fan is an optional unit which can be fitted to cars which are used regularly for towing or in severe climatic conditions. The function of the secondary fan is to prevent excessive use of the electro-magnetic fan. The secondary fan is mounted forward of the radiator, is electrically-operated and acts as the primary cooling fan, the electro-magnetic fan only operating under high temperature conditions when required. The secondary fan can be removed as follows.

2 Disconnect the battery earth (negative) lead.

3 Detach and remove the radiator grille.

4 Detach and remove the front bumper.

5 Detach and remove the sound insulating panel from the front of the engine compartment.

6 Raise and support the car at the front end.

7 Detach and remove the engine undertray.

8 Detach and remove the horns.

9 Disconnect the secondary fan wiring connector, then undo the retaining bolts and nuts and carefully slide the fan unit from the centre cut-out, hook from the radiator flange (to the left of centre) and remove the fan.

10 Refit in the reverse order of removal. Ensure that the wiring connections are securely made and that the loom is routed clear of the fan blades. Check for satisfactory operation of the fan on completion.

18 Expansion tank and coolant level sensor – removal and refitting

1 With the engine cold, turn the expansion tank filler cap 90° in an anti-clockwise direction and release any remaining pressure from the cooling system. Remove the filter cap.

2 Place a suitable container beneath the expansion tank.

3 Disconnect and plug the upper hose(s).

4 Disconnect the coolant level sensor wiring (where applicable).

5 Unscrew the expansion tank retaining bolts and tilt the tank so that the coolant is at the sealed end.

6 Disconnect and plug the lower hose.

7 Drain the expansion tank and remove it.

8 Where applicable, unscrew the collar from the coolant level sensor and withdraw the spacer, sensor and seal. Note that the sensor can only be fitted in one position.

9 Refitting is a reversal of removal. Top up the coolant level to the maximum mark using the recommended antifreeze/corrosion inhibitor mixture. Refit the cap then run the engine at a fast idling speed for several minutes and check the expansion tank for leaks. Stop the engine and top up the coolant level if necessary.

19 Temperature gauge transmitter – removal and refitting

1 The temperature gauge transmitter is located in the outlet side of the thermostat housing. To remove it, first make sure that the engine is cold.

2 Turn the expansion tank filler cap 90° in an anti-clockwise direction to release any remaining pressure from the cooling system, then refit the cap.

3 Disconnect the wire from the terminal on the transmitter (photo).

4 Unscrew and remove the transmitter from the water pump housing and temporarily plug the aperture with a suitable rubber or cork bung.

5 Smear a little sealing compound on the transmitter threads and refit it using a reversal of the removal procedure. Top up the cooling system if necessary.

20   Fault diagnosis – cooling system

Symptom	Reason(s)
Overheating	Low coolant level
	Faulty expansion tank pressure cap
	Thermostat sticking shut
	Drivebelt(s) slipping
	Clogged radiator matrix
	Faulty fan unit
	Blockage in coolant hose
	Cylinder head gasket blown
	Cylinder head or block cracked
	Exhaust system restricted
Overcooling	Thermostat jammed open, missing or of incorrect setting
Slow warm up	Thermostat sticking open
	Faulty fan unit
Coolant loss	Damaged or deteriorated hose
	Leaking water pump or thermostat housing gasket
	Blown cylinder head gasket
	Leaking radiator
	Pressure cap defective or incorrect rating
	Cylinder head or block cracked
	Core plug leak

Chapter 3 Fuel and exhaust systems

Contents

Specifications

General ....
Rear mounted fuel tank, injector pump with integral transfer pump. Glow plug pre-warm. Normally aspirated or turbocharged

Fuel
Fuel type ....
Commercial Diesel fuel for road vehicles (DERV)

Fuel capacity...
60 to 70 litres (13.2 to 15.4 gallons) according to model

Air filter
2.1 litre engine.. Champion W168
2.3 litre engine.. Champion W151
2.5 litre engine (normally aspirated).......................... Champion W151
2.5 litre engine (Turbo) .... Champion type not available

Fuel filter
2.1 litre engine.. Champion L132
2.3 litre engine.. Champion type not available
2.5 litre engine (normally aspirated).......................... Champion L132
2.5 litre engine (Turbo) .... Champion type not available

Injection pump
Type:
    2.1, 2.3 and 2.5 litre (STP type) engines .... DPC Distributor
    2.5 litre (STR and SFA type) engines .... CAV RotoDiesel DPCR
Governor type .... Mechanical (2 speed on DPCR pump)
Plunger opening pressure:
    Normally aspirated engines .... 110 to 120 bar (1595 to 1740 lbf/in^2)
    Turbo engine.. 125 to 135 bar (1813 to 1958 lbf/in^2)

Injectors ....
Pintle

Glow plugs
2.1 litre engine:
    Up to February 1979 .... Champion CH44
    March 1979 on... Champion CH63
2.3 and 2.5 litre engines .... Champion CH68

Adjustment data

Injection pump timing:	
2.1 litre engine	4.91 mm (0.1935 in) 25°BTDC
2.3 litre engine	2.30 mm (0.0906 in) 17°BTDC
2.5 litre engine	2.85 mm (0.1123 in) 18°BTDC
Idle speed:	
Normally aspirated engines	750 to 800 rpm or 800 to 850 rpm* (*2.3 litre from engine no.6004717)
Turbo engine	875 to 900 rpm
Fast idle speed:	
2.1 litre engine	No information available
2.3 and 2.5 litre engines	870 to 920 rpm
Maximum no-load speed	4800 rpm
Deceleration time allowable	5 seconds (maximum no-load speed to idle speed)

Turbocharger .... Garret AiResearch T03

Torque wrench settings

All models

	Nm	lbf ft
Injector-to-cylinder head	90	66
Injector studs	5.0 to 7.0	3.7 to 5.2
Injector retainers	15 to 20	11 to 15
Injector pump bracket bolts	15 to 20	11 to 15
Injector pump to front cover bolts	20 to 25	15 to 18
Injector pump adjuster bolts	15 to 20	11 to 15
Injector pump and retainer to block bolts	5.0 to 7.0	3.7 to 5.2
Automatic idle control	35 to 50	26 to 37
Glow plugs	40	30
Fuel feed pipe bolts	30 to 35	22 to 26
Fast idle temperature sensor	35 to 50	26 to 37
Injector nozzles	70 to 90	52 to 66
Fuel return pipes:		
Brass type	30 to 35	22 to 26
Plastic type	15 to 25	11 to 18
Injector pipe:		
Ermoto type	20 to 30	15 to 22
Guido type	25 to 35	18 to 26
Accelerator cable adjuster locknut	5.0 to 7.5	3.7 to 5.5
Accelerator clamp bolt	4.0 to 5.0	3.0 to 3.7
Inlet manifold retaining bolts	20 to 25	15 to 18
Exhaust manifold retaining bolts	20 to 25	15 to 18
Exhaust downpipe stud nuts	34 to 39	25 to 29
Exhaust system U-clamp nuts	37 to 44	27 to 32

2.5 litre Turbo engine with DPRC pump unit (where different from above)

	Nm	lbf ft
Injector pump gauge mounting plug	10 to 12	7.4 to 8.9
Turbo-to-exhaust manifold bolts	41 to 51	30 to 38
Turbo-to-elbow joint bolts:		
Upper	21 to 29	15 to 21
Lower	48 to 55	35 to 40
Turbo elbow-to-downpipe bolts	30 to 40	22 to 29
Oil return pipe flange bolts	18 to 25	13 to 18

1 General description

The fuel system consists of a rear-mounted fuel tank, a fuel filter, fuel injection pump, injectors and associated components. The exhaust system is similar to that used on petrol-engined vehicles.

Fuel is drawn from the tank by the transfer pump incorporated in the injection pump. En route it passes through the fuel filter, located in the engine bay, where foreign matter and water are removed. The injection pump is gear or chain driven from the crankshaft and supplies fuel under very high pressure to each injector in turn as it is needed. The amount of fuel delivered is determined by the pump governor, which reacts to throttle position and to engine speed. Injection timing is varied automatically to suit the prevailing speed and load.

Rigid pipes connect the pump and injectors. There are four injectors, situated where spark plugs would be found on a petrol engine. Each injector sprays fuel into a pre-combustion or 'swirl' chamber as its piston approaches TDC on the compression stroke. This system is known as indirect injection. The injectors only open under very high pressure. Lubrication is provided by allowing a small quantity of fuel to leak back past the injector internal components. The leaked-back fuel is returned to the pump and then to the fuel tank.

Two systems, both automatic, assist cold starting. A cold-start advance device on the injection pump alters the injection timing and causes fuel delivery to be increased during cold starts. It contains a heating element which is energised when the engine is running. Pre-heater or 'glow' plugs are fitted to each swirl chamber: they are electrically heated before, during and immediately after a cold start. A warning light illuminates when the ignition is switched on, showing that the glow plugs are in operation. When the light goes out, preheating is complete and the engine can be started. The glow plugs are controlled by a special relay which incorporates a temperature sensor.

To stop the engine, a solenoid valve at the rear of the fuel pump is used. The valve is of the 'fail safe' type, so it must be energised to allow the engine to run. When power is removed from the valve, its plunger moves under spring pressure and interrupts fuel delivery.

A Garret AiResearch T03 type turbocharger is fitted to the 2.5 litre engine in the Granada model from November 1988 on. The turbocharger is driven from the exhaust system and is mounted directly underneath the exhaust manifold. Its function is similar to that of a supercharger, to increase engine power and torque, to improve fuel efficiency, and to reduce the engine noise level. The fuel injection system on this engine is much the same as that used on the normally aspirated 2.5 litre engine, the only significant difference being the

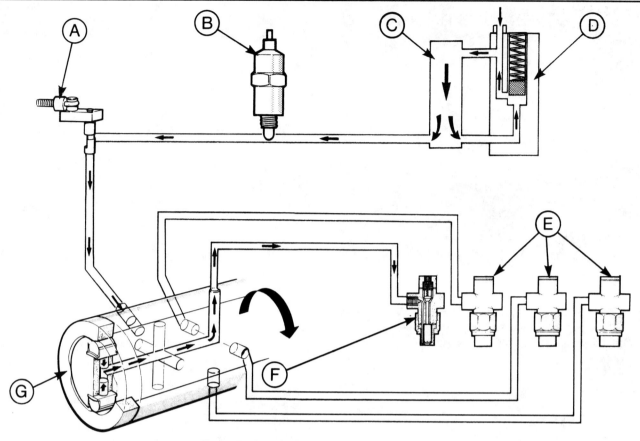

Fig. 3.1 Fuel injection circuit – 2.1 litre engine (Sec 1)

A Main metering valve
B Stop control solenoid
C Transfer pump
D Pressure regulator
E Injectors
F Injector (cutaway view)
G Distribution rotor/plunger
     unit (in pump)

additional fitting of a smoke limiting valve. This measures the turbo boost pressure (via the inlet manifold) and regulates the fuel delivery as required.

The fuel system on Diesel engines is normally very reliable. Provided that clean fuel is used and the specified maintenance is conscientiously carried out, no problems should be experienced. The injection pump and injectors may require overhaul after high mileages have been covered, but this cannot be done on a DIY basis.

2 Routine maintenance

1   At every refuelling, take care not to introduce water or dirt into the fuel tank. Only use commercial Diesel fuel intended for road vehicles (DERV). Do not use marine, agricultural or aviation fuel, nor fuel from anonymous cans or bowsers.

2   In winter it may be necessary to use a fuel additive to prevent fuel waxing. Diesel fuel sold in the UK in winter is normally protected from waxing down to –9°C (+ 16°F). If lower temperatures are expected, add a proprietary anti-waxing additive to the fuel tank as directed by the maker of the additive. The additive is only effective when mixed with the fuel **before** waxing occurs. Note that summer grade fuel in the UK is liable to wax below 0°C (32°F), so it should not be used without anti-waxing additives in winter.

3   The use of petrol or paraffin (kerosene) as an anti-waxing additive is not recommended. Petrol will lower the flashpoint of the fuel to potentially dangerous levels; paraffin cannot be used because it is not taxed as a vehicle fuel.

4   At every major service interval, or more frequently if dictated by local conditions, drain the water layer from the fuel filter as described in Section 4.

5   At the same interval, check the idle speed and adjust if necessary.

6   Every 24 000 miles (40 000 km) or two years, whichever comes first, renew the fuel filter element as described in Section 4.

7   At the same interval, renew the air cleaner element as described in Section 3. More frequent renewal may be necessary if the vehicle is driven in very dusty conditions – eg mostly on unmade roads.

8   Inspect the exhaust system at alternate major service intervals, or whenever excessive noise becomes evident. Refer to Section 18.

9   On Turbo engines, check the oil feed and return pipes of the turbocharger for any signs of oil leakage.

10   Apart from routine inspections for leaks and component security, which should form part of every major service, no other fuel system maintenance is specified.

3 Air cleaner element – renewal

Normally aspirated engines

1   Disconnect the battery earth (negative) lead.

2   Unscrew the retaining nuts and lift the cover from the air cleaner unit, then withdraw the element. If required the air cleaner body can be removed by detaching the hose connections to it and unbolting it from its mounting brackets (photos).

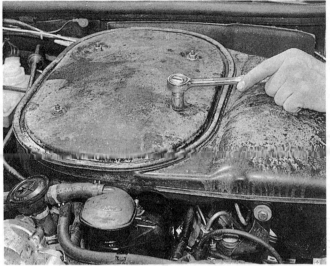

3.2A Unscrew the retaining nuts ...

3.2B ... lift the cover clear ...

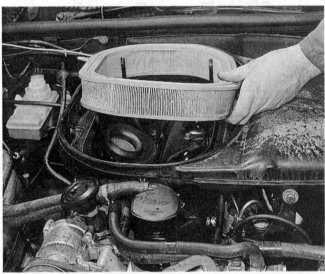

3.2C ... and extract the air filter element (normally aspirated engines)

3.2D Air cleaner mounting bracket (left-hand rear)

3.2E Air cleaner mounting bracket and clamp (inlet manifold side)

3.2F Air cleaner mounting bracket (left-hand front)

3.2G Removing the air cleaner body

3.6B ... lift the air cleaner lid clear ...

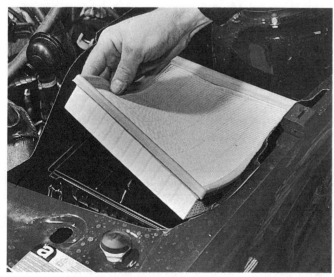

3.6C ... and extract the element (Turbo engine)

3.6A Release the lid clips ...

3   Before inserting the new element, wipe the interior of the cleaner body and the underside of the cover clean.

4   Fit the element into position in the body, refit the cover and if detached, reconnect the hoses to the cleaner body. Reconnect the battery earth lead.

Turbocharged engines

5   Disconnect the battery earth lead.

6   Disconnect the turbo air hose at the air cleaner end. Release the four clips that secure the air cleaner cover and lift the cover clear. Extract the element from the air cleaner body (photos).

7   Wipe clean the interior of the air cleaner body, also the underside of its cover, then insert the new element into position.

8   Refit the cover and fasten the retaining clips. Reconnect the air hose to the air cleaner unit and reconnect the battery earth (negative) lead.

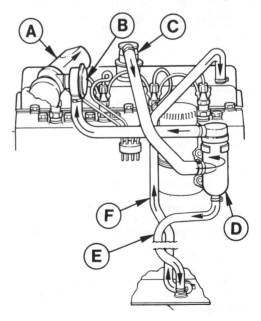

Fig. 3.2 Air cleaner and associated hoses – Turbo engine (Sec 3)

A   *Air cleaner-to-turbo tube*   D   *Oil trap*
B   *Valve*   E   *Sump return line*
C   *Oil filler cap*   F   *Sump-to-rocker cover line*

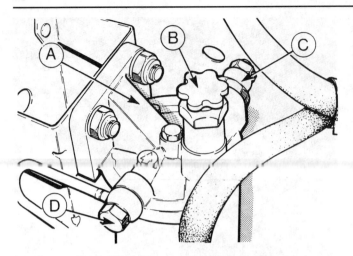

Fig. 3.3 Fuel filter – 2.1 litre engine (Sec 4)

A   Filter head   C   Outlet
B   Hand primer   D   Inlet

4.3 Fuel filter drain plug (2.3 litre engine)

4.4 Fuel filter element removal (2.3 litre engine)

4   Fuel filter – draining and element renewal

1   During operations on the fuel filter, position rags or other suitable materials under the filter body to absorb any fuel spillage.

Draining
2   Disconnect the battery earth (negative) lead.

3   Locate a container beneath the filter drain plug which is positioned in the bottom of the filter. Undo the plug and drain the fuel from the filter into the container. When drained, retighten the drain plug (photo).

Element renewal
4   Support the filter bowl underneath, then unscrew and remove the single retaining bolt from the top of the unit (in the centre). Lower the filter body from the top cover section and remove the body together with the filter (photo).

5   Remove the old filter element, empty any remaining fuel from the body bowl and wipe it clean inside. Remove the old seal rings, one from the outer case groove, the small O-ring from the central post and the seal ring from the lower element support case (as applicable). The seal(s) must always be renewed at the same time as the filter.

6   Locate the new seal(s) into position, then locate the new filter element into the body. Refit the body to the top cover section and tighten the central retaining bolt to secure, but take care not to over-tighten this bolt.

7   Bleed the filter as described in Section 8, then remove the container and rags from under the filter body and reconnect the battery earth lead.

8   When the engine is restarted, check around the filter seal for any signs of leaks.

5   Fuel filter unit – removal and refitting

1   Refer to the previous Section and proceed as described in paragraphs 1 to 3.

2   Unscrew the union bolts and detach the inlet and outlet fuel lines from the filter unit. Move the pipes away from the filter and position them as high as possible to minimize the fuel loss from them.

3   Undo the two retaining nuts and withdraw the fuel filter from its mounting bracket.

4   Refitting is a reversal of removal procedure. Renew the copper sealing washers when reconnecting the inlet and outlet fuel lines to the unit.

5   Refer to Section 8 and bleed the fuel system. Remove the drain container and rags from under the filter when the system is bled, then restart the engine and check for any signs of fuel leaks from the filter connections.

6   Fuel injectors – testing on engine

Warning: *Exercise extreme caution when working on the fuel injectors. Never expose the hands or any part of the body to injector spray, as the high working pressure can cause the fuel to penetrate the skin, with possible fatal results. You are strongly advised to have any work which involves testing the injectors under pressure carried out by a dealer or fuel injection specialist*

1   It is not recommended that any attempt be made to dismantle or repair a fuel injector, as this requires specialist knowledge and equipment and is outside the scope of the home mechanic. The best policy is

to renew a faulty injector or have it reconditioned by a Diesel injection specialist.

2   Should an injector be suspect, the following test may be used to determine whether an injector is the cause of rough running and loss of power.

3   Assuming the engine internal components and cylinder compression pressures to be satisfactory, start the engine and allow it to idle until normal operating temperature is obtained.

4   Now slacken the fuel feed pipe union on each injector in turn and note any variation in engine speed. Repeat this test again with the engine running at a fast idle.

5   If the injector is operating correctly there will be a distinct reduction in engine speed accompanied by obvious roughness. If the injector is faulty there will be very little difference in engine speed when the union is slackened.

6   Having isolated the faulty injector using the above procedure, it may now be removed for renewal or reconditioning as described in Section 7.

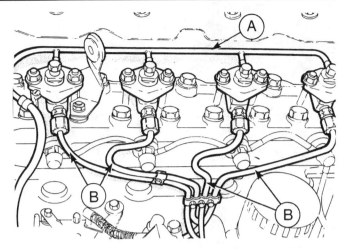

Fig. 3.4 Fuel injectors and pipes layout on the 2.1 litre and early 2.5 litre engines (Sec 7)

A   Leak-off pipe   B   Injector supply pipes

7   Injectors – removal and refitting

1   Disconnect the battery earth (negative) lead.

2   On normally aspirated engines, remove the air cleaner as described in Section 3.

2.1 and 2.5 litre (STF type) engines

3   Unscrew the four retaining bolts and detach the leak-off pipe from the top of each injector.

4   Disconnect the fuel supply from the injectors.

5   Unscrew the two nuts securing the clamp to each injector, remove the clamp and withdraw the injectors. Withdraw the injector heat shield from the cylinder head. The heat shield must be renewed when the injectors are refitted.

6   Prior to refitting the injectors, check that their seatings are perfectly clean, then fit the new heat shield to the cylinder head.

7   Fit the injectors and loosely connect each fuel line to its injector (to ensure correct thread alignment).

8   Refit the clamp to each injector in turn and tighten the retaining nuts.

9   Tighten the fuel line union nuts at the injectors.

10   Reconnect the leak-off pipe to each injector.

11   Reconnect the battery, restart the engine and check for any signs of leakage from the fuel line/injector joints.

2.3 and 2.5 litre (STR and SFA type) engines

12   Unscrew the union nuts and detach the fuel lines to the injectors from the injector pump.

13   Disconnect the injector lines at the injectors and withdraw the fuel leak-off hose, being prepared for fuel spillage (photo). Plug the pipe and pump connections to prevent the ingress of dirt.

14   Unscrew each injector in turn using a suitable socket and remove them together with the copper sealing washers and heat protector washers. As they are removed (and whilst they are removed from the car), take care not to damage the injectors and in particular, their pentle tip. If dropped and damaged, they will need renewal.

7.13 Detach the fuel line, the fuel leak-off hose and harness clip from the injector

7.15A Locate a new copper washer ...

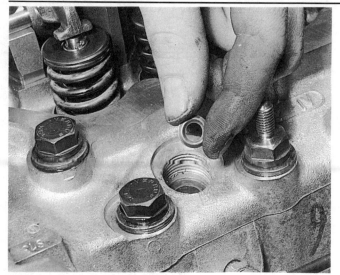

7.15B ... and heat protector washer

7.17 Fit and tighten the injector to the specified torque setting

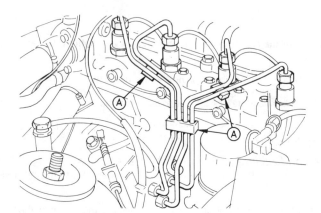

Fig. 3.5 Fuel injector pipes layout on 2.3 litre and later 2.5 litre engines showing locations of the anti-vibration clamps (Sec 7)

A   Anti-vibration clamps

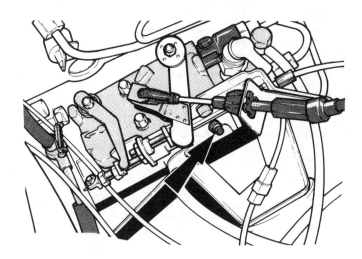

Fig. 3.6 Injector pump bleed bolt (arrowed) – 2.1 litre engine (Sec 8)

15   Renew the heat protector washers and the copper sealing washers irrespective of their condition (photos).

16   Ensure that all connections are perfectly clean prior to refitting the injectors and associate fittings. Remove the blanking plugs.

17   Refitting is a reversal of the removal procedure. As they are fitted, tighten each injector to the specified torque wrench setting (photo). When reconnecting the injector pipe lines, ensure that the anti-vibration clamps are fitted to them (Fig. 3.5).

8   Fuel system – bleeding

1   Disconnect the battery earth (negative) lead.

2   Connect a bleed tube and suitable container to the bleed nipple bolt of the fuel filter.

3   Loosen off the bleed nipple bolt on the fuel outlet union by half-a-turn. Unscrew the hand pump plunger and then actuate it to pump air and fuel from the nipple. When air in the unit is fully purged and only fuel runs from the filter, retighten the nipple bolt (photo).

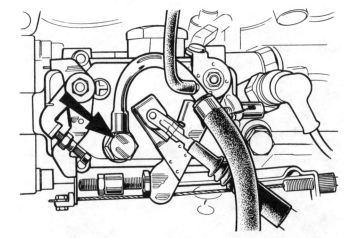

Fig. 3.7 Injector pump bleed bolt – 2.1 litre up to 1985 (Sec 8)

4   On pre-1985 models, the injector pump must also be bled of air. On the 2.1 litre engine a bleed nipple bolt is located towards the rear of the unit (Fig. 3.6). Position some rags or a suitable container in which to catch the fuel, then loosen off the pump bleed nipple bolt. On the 2.5 litre engine loosen off the banjo bolt shown in Fig. 3.7. Actuate the hand

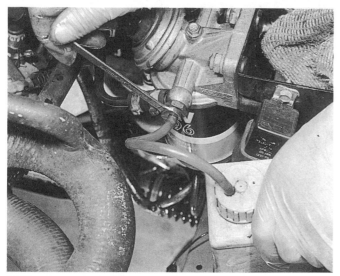

8.3 Bleeding the fuel system

pump plunger on the top of the filter unit and purge any air from the injector pump unit in the same manner as that for the filter, then retighten the bleed nipple bolt or banjo bolt (as applicable).

5   Retighten the hand pump plunger. Remove the drain container and rags from below the filter/injector pump and reconnect the battery.

6   Restart the engine and check for any signs of fuel leaks from the filter and where applicable, the injector pump unit. If the engine is reluctant to start, loosen off the No 1 and No 2 injector pipes and turn the engine over on the starter motor to purge them of air. When the engine attempts to start, retighten the injector lines and the engine should then start.

9   Idle speed – checking and adjustment

1   The usual type of tachometer (rev counter), which works from ignition system pulses, cannot be used on Diesel engines. If it is not felt

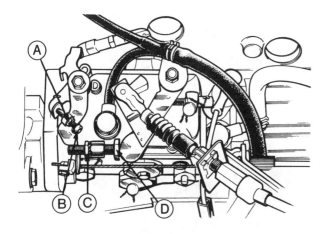

Fig. 3.9 Injection pump (Sec 9)

A	Idle speed adjuster screw locknut	C	Throttle stop adjuster screw locknut
B	Idle speed adjuster screw	D	Throttle stop adjuster screw (anti-stall screw)

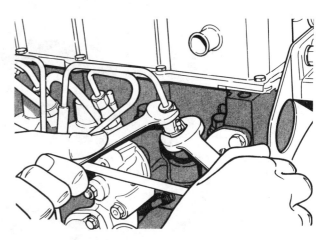

Fig. 3.8 When loosening/removing an injector pipe, secure the injector against turning as shown (Sec 8)

that adjusting the idle speed 'by ear' is satisfactory, one of the following alternatives must be used:

(a)   Purchase or hire of an appropriate tachometer
(b)   Delegation of the job to a Ford dealer or other specialist
(c)   Timing light (strobe) operated by a petrol engine running at the desired speed. If the timing light is pointed at a chalk mark on the Diesel engine crankshaft pulley, the mark will appear stationary when the two engines are running at the same speed (or multiples of that speed)
(d)   Calculating the mph/rpm relationship for a particular gear and running the engine, in that gear, with the front wheels free. The speedometer accuracy may not be adequate, especially at low speeds. Stringent safety precautions must be observed.

2   Before checking and if necessary, making adjustments, warm up the engine until it is at normal operating temperature.

3   Connect the tachometer, if used, or make the necessary alternative arrangements. Start the engine and allow it to idle. Compare the idle speed with that specified.

4   If the idle speed is found to be incorrect, adjust the idle speed control lever setting to suit by loosening off the adjuster screw locknut and then turning the screw in the required direction. When the correct idle speed is reached, retighten the locknut.

5   It is normal practice in Ford workshops to also check the engine maximum no-load speed and the deceleration time to idle when the throttle is released from the maximum no-load speed position.

6   To check the engine no-load speed, fully open the throttle, but **do not** hold the throttle fully open for longer than 5 seconds at a time! The maximum no-load engine speed should be as specified. The maximum no-load speed cannot be adjusted as it is preset during manufacture. Further adjustment may only be undertaken by the pump manufacturer.

7   Accelerate the engine briefly to maximum rpm. Allow it to return to idle, noting the time taken; this should be no more than 5 seconds, but neither should the engine stall. If the deceleration time is too long, turn the anti-stall screw (shown in Fig. 3.9) a quarter-turn away from the pump control lever. If there is a tendency to stall, turn the screw a quarter-turn towards the lever. Repeat the deceleration check, and re-adjust the idle speed if necessary.

10   Glow plugs – removal and refitting

1   Disconnect the battery earth (negative) lead.

2   On normally aspirated engines, remove the air cleaner element (Section 3), then unbolt and remove the air cleaner body from the

10.3 Glow plug removal

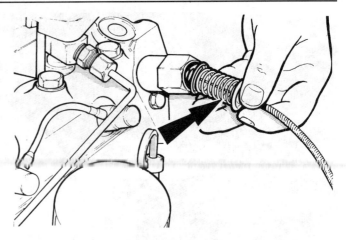

Fig. 3.10 Detaching the idle speed control cable from the sender unit – 2.1 litre engine (Sec 11)

mounting brackets. As it is removed, detach the brake vacuum hose from its location clip on the side of the air cleaner body.

3   Where applicable, detach and remove the terminal covers from the glow plugs. Undo the terminal nut from each terminal, detach the wiring connectors, then unscrew and remove the glow plugs from the cylinder head (photo).

4   Refit in the reverse order of removal. Tighten the glow plugs to the specified torque wrench setting.

11   Cold-start idle speed control cable – removal, refitting and adjustment

1   Disconnect the battery earth (negative) lead.

2.1 litre engine

2   Release the circlip and detach the cable from the sender unit Fig. 3.10.

3   Release the cable from the pump unit by unscrewing the nuts

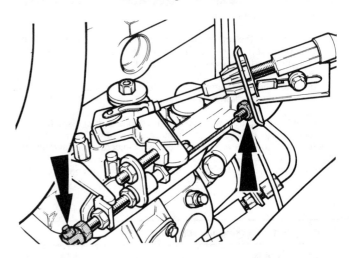

Fig. 3.11 Idle speed cable connections at the fuel injection pump (arrowed) – 2.1 litre engine (Sec 11)

indicated in Fig. 3.11, and detaching the solderless nipple from the idle speed control lever.

11.6A Cold-start sender unit (arrowed)

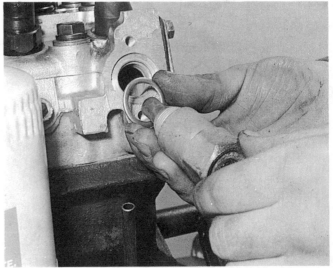

11.6B Cold-start sender unit removal with copper washer

11.7A Cold-start cable locknut at injection pump end

11.7B Cold-start cable withdrawal from adjuster

4   Refit the cable in the reverse order of removal, then set the adjustment as follows.

5   Start the engine and run it until its normal operating temperature is reached. Check that the idle lever is against its stop with the slack just taken out of the cable. If adjustment is necessary, loosen off the cable adjuster and retaining nuts and reset the adjustment to suit. Retighten the cable locknuts.

2.3 and 2.5 litre engines

6   Unscrew the cable sender unit from the cylinder head and retrieve the copper washer (photos). The copper washer must be renewed during reassembly.

7   At the injector pump end, loosen off the cable adjuster locknut then withdraw the cable through the adjuster ferrule (photos).

8   To refit the cable, reverse the removal procedure, but remember to fit a new copper washer to the sender unit. Adjust the cable as follows.

9   Start the engine and warm it up to its normal operating temperature, then with the cable adjuster locknut loosened off, turn the adjuster ferrule to set the lever against its stop, but allowing a 2 mm clearance between the bracket and the cable solderless nipple.

12   Accelerator cable – removal, refitting and adjustment

1   Disconnect the battery earth (negative) lead.

2   Remove the panel from beneath the facia inside the car on the right-hand side.

3   Prise off the clip retaining the cable to the accelerator pedal, and unhook the cable.

4   Working in the engine compartment, release the cable from the bulkhead and pull it through.

5   On normally aspirated engines, detach and remove the air cleaner unit as described in Section 3.

6   Swing the cable pivot/retainer clip from the inner cable and disconnect the inner cable from the throttle lever on the injection pump (photo).

7   Prise the spring clip from the cable bracket using a screwdriver.

8   Depress the four plastic legs and withdraw the cable from the bracket (photo). If difficulty is experienced make up a tool as shown in Fig. 3.12 and push it onto the plastic fitting to depress the legs.

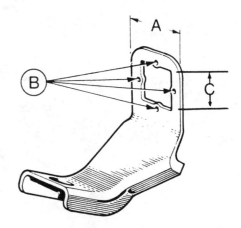

Fig. 3.12 Tool for removing the accelerator cable (Sec 12)

A   25.4 mm (1.0 in)   C   16.0 mm (⅝ in) square hole)
B   Centre punch bolts

12.6 Accelerator cable pivot retaining clip

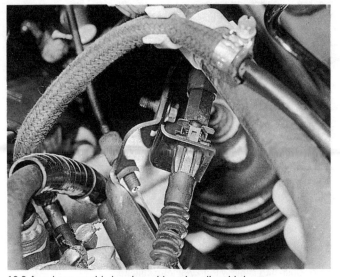

12.8 Accelerator cable bracket with spring clip withdrawn

9   Refitting is a reversal of removal, but before refitting the air cleaner adjust the cable as follows. Using a broom or length of wood fully depress the accelerator pedal and retain it in this position.

10   Unscrew the cable ferrule until the throttle lever segment is fully open. Release the accelerator pedal then fully depress it again and check that the throttle lever segment is fully open.

13   Fuel injection pump – removal and refitting

1   For efficient running of a Diesel engine, accurate fuel injection pump timing is essential. Providing the procedures listed below are strictly followed, it will be possible to remove the fuel injection pump and refit it in its original position. This will be acceptable assuming the timing was correct before removal and the original pump is being refitted. If the pump is to be replaced by a new or reconditioned unit, a number of Ford special tools will be required to accurately set the pump timing prior to fitting. It is therefore recommended that this work be entrusted to your Ford dealer.

2   Disconnect the battery earth (negative) lead.

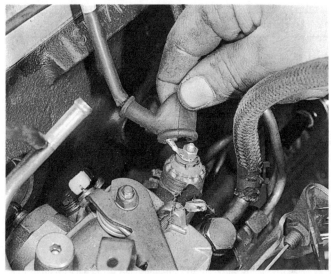

13.5 Disconnect the fuel cut-off solenoid lead

13.7A Detach the fuel lines at the pump ...

13.7B ... and injectors

13.8 Fuel injection pump timing adjustment reference mark

3   On normally aspirated engines, detach and remove the air cleaner body (Section 3).

4   On Turbo engines, detach and remove the air cleaner and crankcase ventilation hoses out of the way from the area above the injection pump. Plug the open end of the turbo inlet air tube to prevent the ingress of dirt.

5   Detach the accelerator cable from the injection pump throttle lever, (Section 12), and the fuel cut-off solenoid lead at the pump (photo).

6   Disconnect the cold-start idle speed control cable from the injection pump as described in Section 11.

7   Clean the fuel line connections at the pump and injectors, then unscrew the union nuts and detach the lines (photos). Disconnect the fuel supply line at the pump, also the leak-off hoses, then plug the ends to prevent the ingress of dirt.

8   The pump timing adjustment is set during manufacture and is made by turning the pump body to the required position, then set by tightening the pump retaining bolts. Before removing the pump it is therefore essential to mark the relative positions of the injection pump and the bearing housing on the rear face of the timing case/interface plate. Make the alignment mark accurately using a centre punch or a scriber as shown (photo). This mark will then act as an alignment guide when refitting the pump to ensure correct timing.

Engines with gear-driven timing components
9   Refer to Chapter 1 and remove the timing case.

10   It is now necessary to rotate the crankshaft until the timing marks on the timing gears are aligned. To reduce the engine compression and enable the crankshaft to be turned more easily, remove the glow plugs from the cylinder head as described in Section 10. To enable the crankshaft to be turned, temporarily refit the crankshaft pulley.

11   Turn the crankshaft until the dots on the timing gears are all adjacent. **Note:** *This only occurs once every 22 revolutions of the crankshaft.*

12   Using a small centre punch, accurately mark the relationship of the injection pump flange to the intermediate mounting flange, and intermediate mounting flange to the timing gear housing. **Note:** *This is most important that these marks are made accurately, otherwise the injection pump timing will be lost when the unit is removed.*

13.13A Fuel injection pump rear support bracket

13.13B Fuel injection pump removal

13.13C Fuel injection pump removed showing master spline (A) on its driveshaft (arrowed). Do not remove cover (B)

13.13D Rear view of the injection pump used on the 2.3 litre engine

13   Undo and remove the bolts securing the pump rear support to the cylinder block, and the pump intermediate flange to the timing gear housing. Now withdraw the pump complete with its timing gear by moving it rearwards and pivoting it toward the engine (photos). Ensure that the engine is not turned over whilst the pump is removed from it or the correct timing may be lost.

Engines with chain-driven timing components

14   With the injection pump timing mark clearly made (paragraph 8), unscrew and remove the pump retaining bolts. These are Allen bolts and require the use of a suitable Allen key to loosen them. On the 2.1 litre engine, hold the top retaining bolt and unscrew the nut on the front side of the timing case. The bottom bolt is also removed from the front on this engine. Support the weight of the pump as the bolts are removed, then withdraw the pump from the engine. Ensure that the engine is not turned over whilst the pump is removed from it or the timing could be lost.

All engines

15   Refitting the fuel injection pump is the reverse sequence to removal, bearing in mind the following points:

   (a)   *On engines with gear-driven timing components, ensure that the crankshaft has not been turned over, and that the timing marks are still in line*

   (b)   *When refitting the pump on engines with chain-driven timing components, ensure that the master splines of the pump and timing sprocket are in alignment*

   (c)   *Position the pump and align the timing marks exactly before tightening the retaining bolts*

   (d)   *Ensure that the fuel line connections are clean before reconnecting them*

   (e)   *When reconnecting, adjust the cold idle speed cable and the accelerator cable as described in Sections 11 and 12 respectively*

   (f)   *When the engine is restarted, check and if necessary adjust the idle speed as described in Section 9*

---

14   Fuel injection pump timing – adjustment

For complete combustion of the Diesel fuel and optimum engine performance a finely controlled amount of fuel must be supplied by the fuel injection pump to the injector of each cylinder when the piston reaches a pre-determined point before TDC on the compression stroke. The position of the crankshaft (in degrees) when the injection pump starts to deliver the fuel is known as the injection pump timing setting. If the timing is incorrect the engine will exhibit various symptoms such as emission of smoke, lack of power, knocking noises etc. It follows, therefore, that whenever the fuel injection pump has been removed, or if any of the timing components such as chain, sprockets or gears are renewed, the timing should be checked and if necessary reset.

Adjustment of the injection pump timing is a complete operation requiring specialist knowledge and instruments, and this work should be entrusted to your Ford dealer. However, once the adjustment has

been carried out the settings should not alter, and further attention will not be necessary unless the injection pump is overhauled or renewed.

---

15   Fuel tank – removal and refitting

1   The removal and refitting procedures for the fuel tank are much the same as those described for the petrol-engine variants of the model concerned. Reference should therefore be made to the Haynes Owners Workshop Manual for the model concerned.

2   The removal and refitting of the fuel gauge sender unit is also described in those manuals.

3   Despite the relative safety of Diesel fuel compared with petrol, repairs to the fuel tank which involve heat **must** be entrusted to a specialist repairer.

4   It should be noted that the fuel tank is vented through a separate pipe, rather than through the filler cap as on petrol engine models.

---

16   Turbocharger – removal and refitting

1   Disconnect the battery earth (negative) lead.

2   Raise and support the car at the front end on axle stands.

3   Detach and remove the engine undershield.

4   Unscrew the retaining nuts and detach the exhaust downpipe from the outlet elbow of the turbo unit (photo).

5   Unscrew and remove the pinch bolt from the steering column/connecting shaft coupling and separate the two (photo).

6   Detach the oil return pipe from the flange connector at the turbo unit and the sump hose. Take care when disconnecting it if the oil is still hot.

7   Detach the air intake tube from the turbo unit. Plug the intake to prevent the ingress of dirt (photo).

8   Loosen off the air intake manifold tube retaining clips and release the tube.

9   Detach the oil feed pipe to the turbo unit and also release it from its location clip at the rear of the cylinder head. Move the pipe clear of the turbo unit, but again taking care if the oil is still hot (Fig. 3.13).

10   Unscrew the four retaining bolts and withdraw the turbo unit downwards from the exhaust manifold and remove it from the underside of the car.

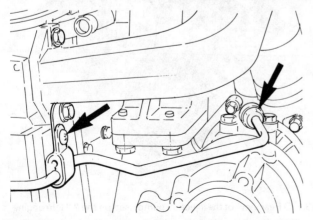

Fig. 3.13 Turbocharger oil feed pipe and retaining clips (Sec 16)

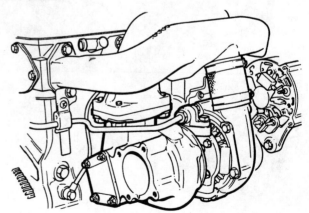

Fig. 3.14 General view of the turbocharger unit and manifolds (Secs 16 and 17)

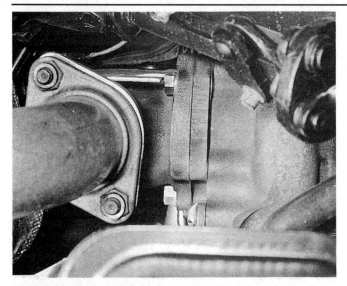

16.4 Exhaust downpipe flange connection to the turbo unit

16.5 Steering column pinch bolt and coupling (arrowed)

location clip at the rear of the engine.

20   Reconnect the air cleaner supply tube to the turbo unit.

21   Reconnect the battery earth (negative) lead, then disconnect the lead from the engine stop solenoid on the fuel pump. Now turn the engine over on the starter motor to the point where the oil pressure warning lamp goes out. This ensures that the turbo bearings are lubricated with oil during the initial start-up period. Failure to observe this procedure could damage the turbo bearings when the engine is restarted. When the oil pressure lamp is extinguished, stop turning the engine over and then reconnect the stop solenoid lead.

22   Restart the engine and check for any signs of oil or exhaust leaks from the turbo and associated connections.

23   Refit the engine undershield and lower the car to the ground.

16.7 Turbo unit and hose connections

11   Clean the mating surfaces of the exhaust manifold and turbo unit. Obtain a new manifold/turbo gasket and also renew the air intake manifold air supply tube and oil return pipe to turbo flange and sump.

12   If a new turbo unit is being fitted, detach the elbow joint from the old turbo unit and fit it to the replacement.

13   Locate the new inlet manifold turbo air supply tube but do not fully tighten the securing clips at this stage.

14   Refit the turbo unit to the exhaust manifold (with new gasket fitted), and tighten the retaining bolts to the specified torque setting in an even manner.

15   Connect the new oil return pipe to the turbo unit and the sump.

16   Connect the exhaust downpipe to the turbo elbow and tighten the retaining nuts to the specified torque.

17   Reconnect the steering shaft to the column coupling and tighten the pinch bolt to the specified torque.

18   Fully tighten the inlet manifold turbo air supply tube retaining clips.

19   Reconnect the oil supply pipe to the turbo unit and secure its

17   Manifolds – removal and refitting

1   Disconnect the battery earth (negative) lead.

Inlet manifold

2   On normally aspirated engines detach and remove the following:

(a)   *The air cleaner unit (Section 3)*
(b)   *Remove the oil filler cap from the rocker cover and move the crankcase ventilation hose and coolant hose clear of the area above the manifolds at the front. Leave the hoses attached, but tie them back out of the way*

3   On Turbo engines, detach and remove the air pipe between the air cleaner and the turbo unit, and the braided hose from the inlet manifold (photo).

4   Undo the retaining bolts and remove the inlet manifold from the cylinder head. On Turbo engines, remove the inlet manifold gasket. Note that a gasket is not fitted to normally aspirated engines.

5   Clean the mating faces of the manifold and cylinder head, then refit the manifold in the reverse order of refitting, but renew the manifold gasket on Turbo engines. Tighten the retaining bolts to the specified torque.

6   Refit the air cleaner/pipe and associate fittings.

Exhaust manifold

7   Remove the inlet manifold as described above.

8   Raise and support the car at the front end on axle stands.

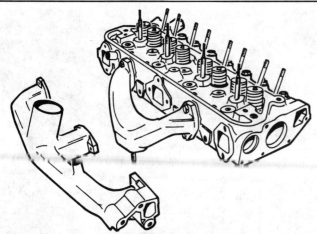

Fig. 3.15 Inlet manifold (removed) and exhaust manifold (attached) (Sec 17)

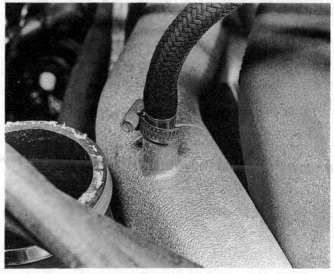

17.3 Braided hose to inlet manifold connection

smear the bolt threads with an anti-seize compound prior to fitting.

15   Refit the inlet manifold as previously described.

16   Reconnect the exhaust downpipe to the manifold or turbo unit (where applicable). Reconnect the oil feed and return pipes and the air intake tube to the turbo unit (where applicable).

17   Restart the engine and check for any signs of leaks from the exhaust manifold connections, then refit the engine undertray and lower the car to the ground.

18   Exhaust system – inspection, removal and refitting

1   The exhaust system should be examined for leaks, damage, and security every 12 000 miles (20 000 km). To do this, apply the handbrake and allow the engine to idle. Lie down on each side of the car in turn and check the full length of the exhaust system for leaks while an assistant temporarily places a wad of cloth over the tailpipe. If a leak is evident, stop the engine and use a proprietary repair kit to seal it. If the leak is excessive or damage is evident, renew the section. Check the rubber mountings for deterioration, and renew them if necessary (photo).

2   To remove the exhaust system jack up the front and rear of the car and support it on axle stands.

3   Unscrew the nuts from the manifold flange, lower the exhaust downpipe and remove the gasket.

4   Disconnect the mounting rubbers and lower the complete system from the car.

5   Refitting is a reversal of removal, but clean the flange mating faces and fit a new gasket. Tighten the flange nuts to the specified torque.

6   Ensure that no part of the exhaust system is less than 25 mm (1.0 in) clear of the underbody and adjacent fittings.

18.1 Check the exhaust system rubber mountings

9   Detach and remove the engine undertray.

10   Unbolt and detach the exhaust downpipe from the exhaust manifold or turbo unit (as applicable).

11   On Turbo engines, refer to Section 16 and disconnect the oil return pipe, the air intake tube and the oil feed pipe from the turbo unit. If required, the turbo unit can be left attached to the exhaust manifold and removed with it (then separated from it later).

12   Undo the retaining bolts and remove the manifold (and turbo unit where applicable). Recover the manifold gasket.

13   Clean the manifold mating faces and obtain a new gasket.

14   Locate the new gasket and fit the manifold. Tighten the retaining bolts evenly to the specified torque setting. Note that it is advisable to

19   Fault diagnosis – fuel system

Symptom	Reason(s)
Engine difficult to start, with emission of black smoke	Defective injectors Fuel injection pump timing incorrect Obstruction in air intake system *See also Chapter 1, 'Fault Diagnosis – engine'*
Engine difficult to start, with no emission of smoke	Fuel tank empty Heater plugs inoperative No fuel output from injection pump Fuel system unprimed 'Stop' control jammed in stop position Fuel filter (or fuel tank vent) clogged Air leak in fuel lines Faulty cold start cable/sensor Poor compressions (see Chapter 1) Defective injection pump or pump timing incorrect
Erratic slow running or stalling	Fuel injection pump idle adjustments incorrect Fuel injection pump timing incorrect Faulty fuel injection pump Worn fuel injectors
Lack of engine power	Fuel injection pump timing incorrect Deferred injection accumulator out of adjustment (where fitted) Air intake partially blocked Faulty fuel injection pump Faulty fuel injector/s Fuel filter clogged *See also Chapter 1, 'Fault diagnosis – engine'*
Engine emits excessive smoke on acceleration	Fuel injection pump timing incorrect Worn fuel injectors Faulty fuel injection pump Engine worn internally
Excessive fuel consumption	Fuel leakage Air cleaner blockage Faulty injector(s) Injection pump timing incorrect
Excessive knocking	Faulty injectors Injection pump timing incorrect Excessive carbon deposits

Chapter 4 Clutch and transmission

Contents

Specifications

Clutch

Type..	Single dry plate, diaphragm spring, cable operation. Automatic adjustment

Clutch plate diameter:
- Sierra.. 242 mm (9.5 in)
- Granada up to 1985... 216 mm (8.5 in)
- Granada 1986 on .... 232 mm (9.1 in)

Clutch lining thickness:
- Granada up to 1985... 3.85 mm (0.152 in)
- Granada (1986 on) and Sierra .... 3.81 mm (0.150 in)

Transmission

Type:
- Granada up to 1982... Ford type 'B' Heavy Duty transmission, four forward speeds and one reverse. Synchromesh on all forward gears.
- Granada 1982 on all Sierra models....................................... Ford type 'N' transmission, five forward speeds and one reverse, synchromesh on all forward gears
- Granada Turbo .... Ford MT75 transmission, five forward speeds and one reverse. Full synchromesh

Ratios:

	Granada up to 1982	Granada 1982 to 1985	Sierra	Granada 1986 on	Granada Turbo
1st.....................	3.358:1	3.904:1	3.91:1	3.65:1	3.61:1
2nd....................	1.809:1	2.32:1	2.32:1	1.97:1	2.08:1
3rd.....................	1.258:1	1.40:1	1.40:1	1.37:1	1.36:1
4th.....................	1.00:1	1.00:1	1.00:1	1.00:1	1.00:1
5th.....................	–	0.816:1	0.82:1	0.816:1	0.83:1
Reverse	3.365:1	3.66:1	3.66:1	3.66:1	3.26:1

Lubricant type/specification:
- Four-speed .... Gear oil, viscosity SAE 80 EP, to Ford spec SQM-2C 9008-A (Duckhams Hypoid 80)
- Five-speed .... Semi-synthetic gear oil, viscosity SAE 80 EP to Ford spec ESD-M2C 175-A (Duckhams Hypoid 75W/90S)

Lubricant capacity:
- Sierra.. 1.9 litres (3.3 pints)
- Granada (up to 1985).. 1.7 litres (3.0 pints)
- Granada (1986 on) .... 1.2 litres (2.1 pints)

Torque wrench settings
Clutch

	Nm	lbf ft
Clutch plate-to-flywheel bolts:		
Granada up to 1985	18	13
Granada (1986 on) and Sierra	20 to 25	15 to 18
Clutch housing-to-engine bolts:		
Granada up to 1985	39 to 48	29 to 35
Granada (1986 on) and Sierra	40 to 50	30 to 37
Clutch housing-to-transmission housing bolts:		
Granada up to 1985	58 to 69	43 to 51
Granada (1986 on) and Sierra	70 to 90	52 to 66

Torque wrench settings (continued)

Transmission

	Nm	lbf ft
'B' type transmission (Granada up to 1982):		
Input shaft bearing retainer	9 to 11	7 to 8
Extension housing-to-transmission bolts	44 to 46	33 to 34
Transmission housing cover bolts	9 to 11	7 to 8
Transmission crossmember-to-floor nuts	20 to 25	15 to 18
Crossmember mounting bush	16 to 20	12 to 15
Transmission mounting bush	50 to 57	37 to 42
'N' type transmission (Granada 1982 to 1985):		
Extension housing-to-transmission	45 to 49	33 to 36
Reversing light switch	1 to 2	0.7 to 1.5
Transmission housing cover bolts	9 to 11	7 to 8
Selector lock mechanism	17 to 19	13 to 14
Oil filler/level plug	23 to 27	17 to 20
5th gear collar nut	120 to 150	89 to 110
5th gear lock plate	21 to 26	16 to 19
Gear lever-to-extension housing bolts	21 to 26	16 to 19
'N' type transmission (Granada 1986 on and Sierra):		
Clutch guide sleeve	9 to 11	7 to 8
Transmission cover	10 to 13	7 to 9
Crossmember	20 to 25	15 to 18
Insulator to crossmember	16 to 20	12 to 15
Insulator to gearbox	50 to 57	37 to 42
Reversing light switch	1 to 2	0.7 to 1.5
Selector interlock	17 to 19	13 to 14
Filler plug	33 to 41	24 to 30
5th gear collar nut	120 to 150	89 to 110
5th gear lock plate	21 to 26	15 to 19
Selector lever to extension housing	21 to 26	15 to 19
MT75 type transmission (Granada Turbo):		
Engine/transmission mounting-to-transmission bolts	52 to 71	38 to 52
Transmission crossmember-to-floor bolts	30 to 40	22 to 29
Torx studs to vibration damper	70 to 90	51 to 66
Driveshaft to Torx stud nuts	70 to 85	51 to 63
Driveshaft-to-transmission output flange bolts	76 to 82	56 to 60
Transmission housing-to-engine bolts	70 to 90	51 to 66
Gearshift support bracket (to transmission)	21 to 25	15 to 18
Gearshift gate-to-transmission bolts	8 to 11	6 to 8
Reversing light switch	10 to 14	7 to 10
Drain plug/oil filler plug	29 to 41	21 to 30

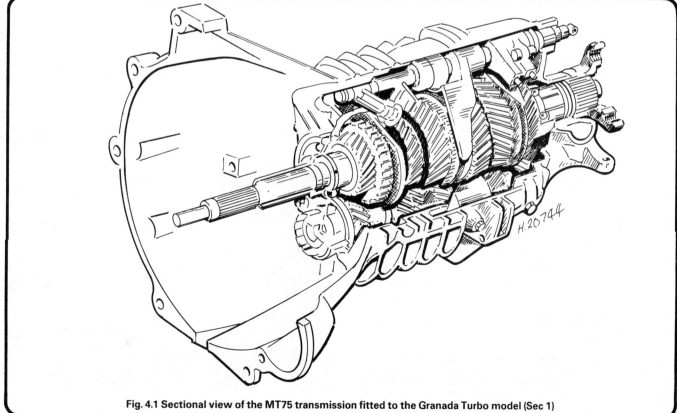

Fig. 4.1 Sectional view of the MT75 transmission fitted to the Granada Turbo model (Sec 1)

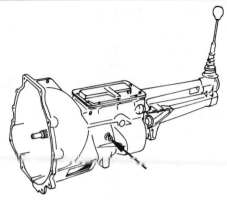

Fig. 4.2 The 'B' type transmission unit showing location of the filler/level plug (arrowed) (Sec 2)

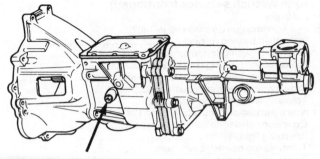

Fig. 4.3 The 'N' type transmission unit showing location of the filler/level plug (arrowed) (Sec 2)

1   General description

1   The transmission and associated components fitted to the Diesel models are in most instances identical to those used in the petrol-engined variants. Drive from the engine to the transmission is transferred by a single plate clutch. The clutch is cable-operated and its adjustment is automatic on all models.

2   The transmission fitted to the earlier Granada models (up to 1982) is the Ford type 'B', four-speed transmission. The Sierra and later Granadas (except Granada Turbo) are fitted with the Ford 'N' type five-speed transmission. The Granada Turbo is fitted with the five-speed Ford MT75 type transmission (Figs. 4.1),

3   The basic specifications concerning each of these transmission types are given at the start of this Chapter. The overhaul details for the 'B' and 'N' type transmissions are described in the appropriate model-specific owners workshop manual. The overhaul details for the MT75 type transmission are not described.

2.5 Oil filler/level plug (A) and oil drain plug (B) – MT75 transmission

2   Routine maintenance

Clutch
1   Clutch adjustment is automatic in use, by means of a ratchet device at the clutch pedal. If the pedal free play becomes excessive, this can be corrected by lifting the pedal as far as its stop and then releasing it.

2   No other routine maintenance is specified for the clutch. If the cable becomes stiff or jerky it must be renewed. Components such as the clutch release bearing and the driveplate should be inspected if they become accessible during other operations, and renewed if necessary.

Transmission
3   Check and if necessary, top up the transmission oil level at the intervals specified in the *Routine Maintenance* section at the start of this manual. Check the level as follows.

4   With the vehicle parked on level ground, locate the oil filler/level plug shown in Fig. 4.2 or 4.3 (photo). If it is necessary to raise the vehicle in order to gain access to the plug, maintain its level attitude as far as is possible and ensure that it is securely supported. Wipe around the plug, then unscrew and remove it.

5   The oil level should be level with the base of the plug hole. A length of wire bent at a right angle at one end will serve as a suitable dipstick. Top up the oil level if necessary with oil of the correct grade. When oil starts to drip out of the hole, refit the plug and tighten it. Wipe clean any oil spillage from around the filler/level plug area (photo).

6   Check for oil leaks from the transmission. Renew oil seals or repair any other damage as necessary.

7   Oil changing is not considered necessary as a routine operation. Should it be necessary to drain the transmission for any reason, the oil is best syphoned out through the filler/level plug hole as there is no oil drain plug fitted (except on the MT75 transmission).

3.1A Clutch disc showing 'FLYWHEELSIDE' mark – Sierra

3.1B Showing clutch disc orientation and centralising tool – Sierra

3.1C Clutch pressure plate is located over the flywheel dowels – Sierra

3.2 Clutch release arm and bearing – Sierra

3.3 Tighten the clutch fastenings to the specified torque settings

3 Clutch – removal, inspection and refitting

1 The removal, inspection and refitting procedures for the clutch unit and release bearing are in general the same as those described for the petrol engine versions. Some minor physical differences exist, an example being shown in the accompanying photographs of the Sierra clutch. With this model the clutch disc orientation mark is on the inner pressure plate side of the disc so that when fitted the disc is as shown (photos).

2 The clutch release arm also differs in appearance to the arm used on the petrol engine version, but its removal and refitting details are the same (photo).

3 When securing the clutch and related components, tighten the fastenings to the torque wrench settings given in the Specifications at the start of this Chapter (photo).

4 'B' and 'N' type transmissions – removal and refitting

1 The removal and refitting procedures for these transmission types are the same as described for petrol engine models. Only the following

items differ, on the Sierra model.

2 The air cleaner unit will need to be removed. Refer to Chapter 3 in this manual for details.

3 Undo the retaining bolts, release the clips and remove the radiator upper shroud.

4 The starter motor can be detached but left attached to the engine bracket by removing the upper retaining bolt but loosening the two lower bolts. When removing the clutch housing adaptor plate, note that it is secured by three bolts and the upper bolt also secures the battery cable bracket.

5 MT75 type transmission – removal and refitting

1 Disconnect the battery earth (negative) lead.

2 Unclip and remove the engine sound insulation panels from each side at the front (Fig. 4.4).

3 Unbolt and remove the upper and lower sections of the radiator shroud.

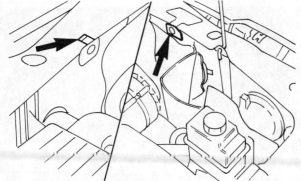

Fig. 4.4 Release the clips arrowed to remove the engine sound insulation panels from the left and right-hand sides (Sec 4)

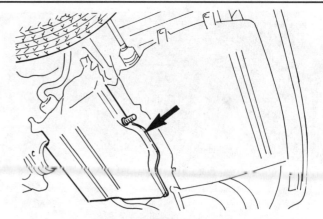

Fig. 4.5 Remove the sound insulation panel (arrowed) beneath the transmission (Sec 5)

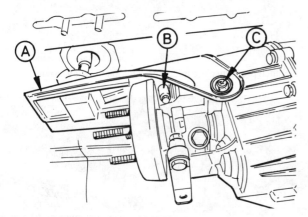

Fig. 4.6 Gearshift support bracket (A), shift rod coupling (B) and retaining bolt (C) (Sec 5)

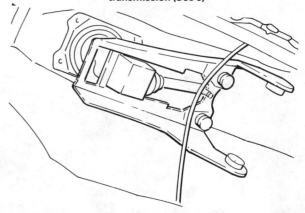

Fig. 4.7 Support the bracket as shown with a length of rod (Sec 5)

4   Unscrew the starter motor upper retaining bolts and detach the earth lead.

5   Raise and support the car at the front end on axle stands.

6   Unclip and remove the sound insulation panel from the underside of the engine/transmission (Fig. 4.5).

7   Undo the two retaining nuts and detach the exhaust downpipe from the turbo unit. Support the exhaust system, disengage it from the

support straps and remove it from under the car (photo).

8   Unscrew the retaining bolts and detach the anti-roll (stabilizer) bar from the underbody mounting each side.

9   Mark the propeller (drive) shaft centre and rear coupling flanges for alignment then undo the four bolts securing it to the rear axle and the two bolts securing it to the centre bearing.

10   Unscrew and remove the three nuts securing the shaft to the transmission output flange coupling (photo), then lower and remove the

5.7 Disconnect the exhaust system from the support straps (arrowed)

5.10 Propeller shaft-to-transmission front coupling nuts (arrowed)

5.16 Gearshift support bracket-to-transmission bolt and reversing lamp switch lead connection (MT75 transmission)

5.18 Starter motor-to-MT75 transmission bolts

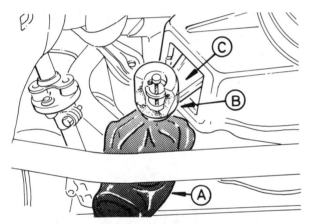

Fig. 4.8 Clutch cable and lever – MT75 transmission (Sec 5)

A   Gaiter   B   Damping weight   C   Release lever

shaft from under the car. Unless they are to be removed, hold the three studs secure as the nuts are unscrewed using a suitable Torx socket. If the transmission is not being overhauled, the damper unit can remain fitted to the rear output flange.

11   Support the clutch pedal with a suitable wood block.

12   Support the weight of the engine using a support bar if possible, but failing this, attach a lift sling and hoist. Do not lift the engine, only take its weight.

13   Position a jack underneath the transmission and raise it to support its weight. Use a trolley-jack if possible as this will be of assistance during the actual removal of the transmission.

14   Unscrew the four retaining nuts securing the transmission crossmember to the floor and the single bolt in the centre securing the crossmember to the transmission.

15   Slowly lower the transmission support jack. As it is lowered, ensure that the engine is clear of the bulkhead and that the cylinder head does not come into contact with the brake pipes. Position a suitable piece of wood between the bulkhead and the head to ensure that the brake pipes are not damaged. If may be necessary to lower the engine support hoist to allow the engine and transmission to be lowered sufficiently.

16   Working from underneath, reach up and detach the gearshift support bracket from the transmission (photo) and detach the shift rod from its coupling (see Fig. 4.6). When disconnected, support the gearshift support bracket in suspension using a suitable length of stiff wire rod as illustrated in Fig. 4.7.

17   Detach the reversing light switch and, where applicable, the speed sensor lead multi-plug connector from the transmission.

18   Disconnect the wiring from the starter motor, undo the retaining bolts and withdraw the starter motor (photo).

19   Prise free the clutch release lever gaiter, then detach the cable from the lever. Remove the damping weight circlip (Fig. 4.8).

20   Undo the three retaining bolts and detach the engine/transmission adaptor plate.

21   Unscrew and remove the engine-to-transmission flange retaining bolts.

22   Check that all of the associated fittings are detached from the transmission, then with the aid of an assistant to help steady transmission as it is withdrawn, pull it rearwards from the engine. The weight of the transmission is considerable and this must be taken into account as it is separated from the engine and lowered for removal from under the car. Ensure that the input shaft is clear of the clutch before tilting and lowering the transmission away from the engine. Initially the two units may prove difficult to separate due to the tightness of the engine-to-clutch housing locating dowels. In this instance carefully tap and prise the transmission from the engine at the flange face, but take care not to damage the clutch housing.

23   Refitting is in general a reverse of the removal procedure, but note the following special points.

24   If the transmission rear flange damper was removed, clean the threads in the damper and the stud threads of dirt and grease. Apply a drop of thread-locking compound to each side of the stud thread, fit the studs and tighten them to the damper (within five minutes of applying the compound).

25   If the damper was not removed from the rear flange, check that the studs are secure by checking that they are tightened to the specified torque wrench setting using a Torx socket and wrench. If any studs are found to be loose they must be removed, cleaned and refitted as described in paragraph 24.

26   Ensure that the engine-to-transmission location dowels are in position.

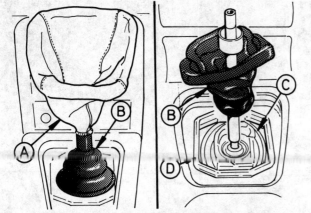

Fig. 4.9 Gear lever outer gaiter (A), inner gaiter (B), retainer frame (C) and insulator pad (D) (Sec 5)

27   Lightly smear the input shaft splines and the guide sleeve with grease prior to refitting the transmission.

28   When assembling the transmission to the engine, the flywheel may have to be turned a fraction to align the splines of the input shaft and the clutch disc and thus allow engagement.

29   Tighten the securing bolts and nuts to the specified torque wrench settings.

30   Where the driveshaft rubber coupling is marked "GAF 30", lubricate the washers on each side with grease.

31   On completion, but before refitting the engine/transmission sound insulation panels, top up the transmission oil level. Restart the engine and check the exhaust system for any signs of leaks, then refit the sound insulation panels.

32   Finally, check that the gear selection is satisfactory. It may be that the gear lever gaiter is ill-fitting, in which case remove the knob from the lever by unclipping it sideways (not by unscrewing it), then release the gaiter from the console and withdraw it. Remove the inner gaiter and check that the insulator pad is correctly located. Refit the inner gaiter and clip the frame into position. Fit the outer gaiter, the console (if detached) and, finally the lever knob by pressing it into position (Fig. 4.9).

Chapter 5 Braking system

Contents

Specifications

System type .... Dual line hydraulic, vacuum servo with pump assistance. Self-adjusting front disc brakes with drum or disc brakes at the rear (depending on model). Mechanical handbrake to rear wheels only. ABS braking system optional on Sierra, standard on Granada 1986 on

Front brakes

	Granada up to 1985	Granada 1986 on and Sierra
Disc diameter	262 mm (10.3 in)	240 mm (9.4 in)
Minimum disc thickness..............................	Not specified	22.8 mm (0.898 in)
Maximum disc run-out................................	0.09 mm (0.0035 in)	0.15 mm (0.006 in)
Minimum pad thickness	1.5 mm (0.060 in)	1.5 mm (0.060 in)
Caliper cylinder diameter	54 mm (2.13 in)	54 mm (2.13 in)

Rear drum brakes

Application.. Granada (up to 1985) and Sierra (non-ABS)

Drum diameter:

Granada Saloon and Sierra................................ 228.6 mm (9.0 in)

Granada Estate... 254 mm (10.0 in)

Minimum lining thickness .... 1.0 mm (0.040 in)

Wheel cylinder diameter:

Granada (Saloon/Estate).................................... 22.2 mm (0.875 in)

Sierra.. 20.6 mm (0.811 in)

Rear disc brakes

Application.. Granada (1986 on) and Sierra (with ABS)

Disc diameter .... 252.7 mm (9.95 in)

Minimum disc thickness.................................... 8.9 mm (0.350 in)

Minimum disc run-out....................................... 0.15 mm (0.006 in)

Minimum disc thickness variation .... 0.15 mm (0.006 in)

Brake fluid (all models) .... Hydraulic fluid to Ford spec SAM-6C 9103 A (Duckhams Universal Brake and Clutch Fluid)

Torque wrench settings

	Nm	lbf ft
Granada (up to 1985)		
Caliper-to-stub axle bolts	65 to 75	48 to 55
Disc-to-hub bolts	54 to 67	40 to 50
Rear brake back plate-to-axle bolts	20 to 24	15 to 18
Hydraulic unions..	7 to 9	5 to 6.5
Sierra		
Caliper suspension knuckle.....................................	51 to 61	38 to 45
Servo unit-to-bulkhead nuts....................................	35 to 45	26 to 33
Master cylinder-to-servo unit nuts	20 to 25	15 to 18
Caliper slide pin bolts (ventilated discs).................	20 to 25	15 to 18

Torque wrench settings (continued)
Granada (1986 on) and Sierra with rear disc brakes and ABS
As above but with the following differences:

	Nm	lbf ft
Rear caliper anchor bracket bolts	51 to 61	37 to 45
Rear caliper slide pin bolts	31 to 35	23 to 26
Rear hub flange nut	250 to 290	184 to 214
Hydraulic actuator unit to bulkhead nuts	41 to 51	30 to 38
Accumulator to pump housing bolt	36 to 46	27 to 34
Pump mounting bolt	7 to 9	5 to 6.5
High pressure pipe union:		
Sierra	7 to 12	5 to 9
Granada	16 to 24	12 to 18
Wheel sensor bolt (front and rear)	8.5 to 11	6 to 8
Reservoir mounting bolt (Granada)	4 to 6	3 to 4.5

1 General description

The standard braking system is conventional is design. The brake pedal operates the front disc brakes and the rear drum brakes by means of a dual circuit hydraulic system with servo assistance. The handbrake operates on the rear brakes only by means of cables. Both the front and rear brakes are self-adjusting in normal use.

All Granada models from 1986 on, and some Sierra models, are fitted with Ford's anti-lock braking system (ABS). As its description implies, the system prevents the wheels from locking up under heavy braking and in adverse road conditions. These models have disc brakes at the rear. The other main differences to the standard brake system are the hydraulic unit and the addition of wheel sensors and an electronic control unit.

Because there is no throttling of the inlet manifold on the Diesel engine, it is not a suitable source of vacuum for the servo operation. The vacuum on non-ABS equipped models is therefore derived from a separate belt driven vacuum pump. On ABS equipped models, an electric pump is combined with the main hydraulic unit to provide the servo vacuum.

Except as noted in this Chapter, the overhaul and repair procedures for the various components in the braking system are described in the appropriate model-specific manual for petrol engine cars.

2 Routine maintenance

1   The maintenance procedures for the braking system are as described for the equivalent petrol engine model, but with the following additional servicing requirement on models with a standard (non-ABS) braking system (photos).

2   Check the vacuum pump for security and the vacuum hoses for condition. Check the vacuum pump drivebelt for condition and tension adjustment. If the drivebelt is in need of adjustment of renewal, refer to Chapter 2 in this manual for details.

3 Vacuum pump – removal, refitting and drivebelt adjustment

1   Disconnect the battery earth (negative) lead.

Granada (up to 1985)
2   Loosen off the vacuum supply hose retaining clip at the pump end and pull free the hose from its connection (Fig. 5.1).

3   Detach the dump hose from the pump unit or manifold. This hose is an interference fit only (no clip) and if found to be a slack fit, it must be renewed. It is important to note that the pump must not be operated with the hoses disconnected or the pump may be seriously damaged.

4   Unscrew and remove the pump adjuster bolts and their flat washers. Loosen the mounting, then pivot the pump to loosen off the drivebelt tension. Disengage the drivebelt from the pump pulley. Unscrew the retaining bolts and remove the pump unit.

Granada (1986 on) and Sierra (1985 on)
5   On later models the pump unit was modified and a support bracket fitted. The removal procedures are otherwise the same as those described for the earlier models (Figs. 5.2 and 5.3).

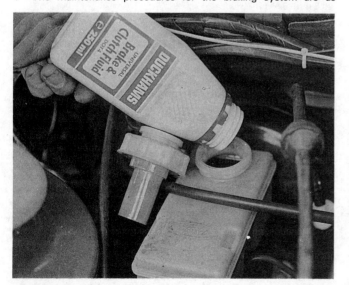
2.1A Topping-up the brake fluid level – Sierra

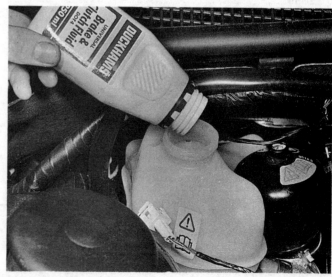
2.1B Topping-up the brake fluid level – Granada Turbo (with ABS)

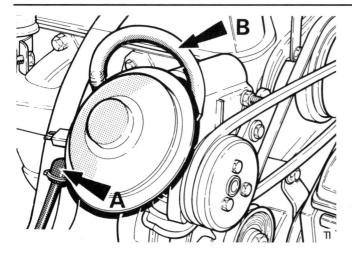

Fig. 5.1 Vacuum pump and hose connections on the early Granada models (Sec 3)

A   Supply hose   B   Dump hose

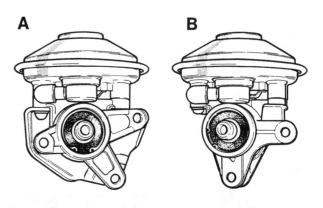

Fig. 5.2 Identification features of the early (A) and late (B) type vacuum pump fitted to the Sierra (early) and Granada models (Sec 3)

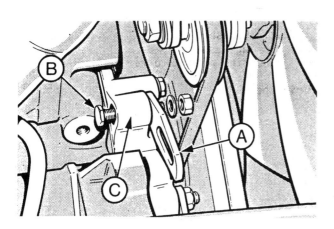

Fig. 5.3 Showing vacuum pump tensioner bracket (A), 35 mm bolt (B) and mounting position (C) on 1985 on Sierra and Granada models (Sec 3)

3.7 The vacuum pump and connections of the later (1987 on) Sierra

Sierra (1987 on)

6   The Sierra was fitted with a later type pump unit, the removal details being as follows.

7   Unscrew the union nuts and disconnect the oil supply line and the vacuum line at their connections to the pump unit. Unscrew the oil return hose clamp and detach the hose from the pump (photo).

8   Loosen off the pump mounting bolts, pivot the pump to slacken off the drivebelt tension and disengage the belt from the pump pulley. Unscrew the bolts and remove the pump (photo).

All models

9   Refitting is a reversal of the removal procedure but note the following:

(a) If the pump is to be renewed on an earlier model Granada, it is probable that a later type pump unit will be supplied, in which case the support bracket/adjuster kit and later type drivebelt will also be required to suit

(b) If the pump hoses or rigid lines (later Sierra) are in dubious condition, or are known to be defective, they must be renewed

(c) Renew the drivebelt if it is worn or cracked. Adjust it for tension as described in Chapter 2

3.8 Vacuum pump removal (late model Sierra)

Chapter 6
Propeller shaft, rear axle and driveshafts

Contents

Specifications

General
Propeller shaft type .... Two or three-piece, tubular, centre bearing with Hardy Spicer universal joints and/or rubber couplings
Final drive type .... Hypoid, bolted to rear underbody and to rear axle beam
Driveshaft type .... Open, tubular, constant velocity (CV) joint at each end

Final drive ratio
Sierra 3.38:1
Granada (up to 1985):
    Standard 3.89:1
    Optional 4.11:1
Granada (1985 on):
    Standard 3.62:1
    Trailer package 3.92:1
    Limited slip differential .... 3.64:1 or 3.92:1

Final drive adjustment
Crownwheel pinion backlash:
    Sierra:
        Normal axle .... 0.08 to 0.15 mm (0.0032 to 0.0059 in)
        Axle with viscous coupling .... 0.10 to 0.17 mm (0.0039 to 0.0067 in)
    Granada (up to 1985):
        Nominal value .... 0.12 to 0.22 mm (0.0047 to 0.0087 in)
        Setting value .... 0.12 to 0.14 mm (0.0047 to 0.0055 in)
    Granada (1985 on):
        Nominal value .... 0.08 to 0.15 mm (0.0032 to 0.0059 in)
Differential bearing preload:
    Sierra .... 4 to 5 teeth
    Granada (up to 1985) .... 0.14 to 0.21 mm (0.0055 to 0.0082 in)
    Granada (1985 on) .... 4 to 5 teeth

Lubricant type/specification .... Hypoid gear oil, viscosity SAE 90 EP to Ford spec SQM-2C 9002-AA or 9003-AA (Duckhams Hypoid 90S)

Torque wrench settings
Sierra

	Nm	lbf ft
Final drive unit cover	45 to 60	33 to 44
Oil filler plug	35 to 45	26 to 33
Crownwheel-to-differential bolts	75 to 90	55 to 66
Drive pinion bearing nut (maximum):		
6.5 in crownwheel	120	88
7.0 in crownwheel	140	103
Pinion flange nut	100 to 120	74 to 89
Driveshaft nut	250 to 290	185 to 214
Final drive-to-crossmember	70 to 90	51 to 66
Axle shafts-to-flange bolts	38 to 43	28 to 32
Axle shafts-to-driveshaft stub	38 to 43	28 to 32

Torque wrench settings (continued)

	Nm	lbf ft
Granada (up to 1985)		
Axle housing cover bolts	45 to 50	33 to 37
Oil filler plug	40 to 50	30 to 37
Axle housing-to-differential extension bolts	70 to 80	52 to 59
Crossmember-to-differential extension bolts	71 to 92	53 to 68
Driveshaft socket-headed bolts	38 to 43	28 to 32
Rear hub centre nut	241 to 261	178 to 193
Bearing hub-to-suspension arm bolts	40 to 50	30 to 37
Granada (1986 on)		
Pinion flange nut:		
1986	110 to 130	81 to 96
1987 on	100 to 120	74 to 89
Final drive mountings:		
To crossmember	70 to 90	52 to 66
Rear mounting to casing	40 to 50	30 to 37
Rear mounting to floor	20 to 25	15 to 18
Final drive cover screws	45 to 60	33 to 44
Final drive oil filler/level plug	35 to 45	26 to 33
Driveshaft flange screws	38 to 43	28 to 32
Rear hub centre nut	250 to 290	185 to 214

1 General

1   The propeller shaft, rear axle and driveshafts fitted to the Diesel engine models covered are in most instances identical to those used on their petrol engine counterparts, the exception being the propeller shaft of the Granada Turbo model. The special differences concerning this are described in the following Section.

2   In all other instances, reference can therefore be made to the appropriate workshop manual for the petrol engine model for details concerning maintenance, removal, refitting and overhaul procedures of these items.

3   Refer to the Specifications at the start of this Chapter for the relevant data concerning the Diesel engine models.

2 Propeller shaft (Granada Turbo) – general

1   As previously mentioned, the propeller shaft on this model is similar in design to that fitted to other Granada models, but the front coupling differs in combining an anti-vibration damper unit. When disconnecting/reconnecting the propeller shaft at the front coupling on this model, refer to paragraphs 10, 25 and 30 of Section 5 in Chapter 4 of this manual for the relevant details.

2   Whenever this type of driveshaft is removed, check if the front rubber coupling is marked "GAF 30", in which case carefully inspect the four rubber spokes of the three bushes. If they show any signs of cracking, the coupling and driveshaft complete must be renewed. Cracks in the rubber skin on the crescent shape are normal and can be ignored.

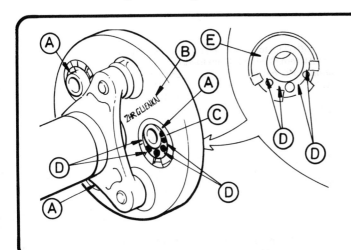

Fig. 6.1 Propeller shaft front coupling (rubber GAF type) as fitted to Granada Turbo model showing (Sec 2)

A   Metal bush
B   Identification mark
C   Crescent shape slot
D   Rubber 'spokes'
E   Rubber skin (on front of crescent slot)

Chapter 7 Suspension and steering

Contents

Specifications

Suspension type

Front:

Granada (up to 1985) .... Independent, coil spring, unequal length swinging arms. Double-acting telescopic shock absorbers.

Granada (1986 on) and Sierra .... Independent, MacPherson struts and anti-roll bar. Double-acting telescopic shock absorbers incorporated in struts

Rear (all models) .... Independent, semi-trailing arms, coil springs and double-acting shock absorbers. Anti-roll bar and ride height control optional on some models

Steering type

All models .... Rack and pinion, power-assisted on some models

Front wheel alignment

Sierra:

Toe setting:

Checking .... 0.5 mm (0.02 in) toe-out to 4.5 mm (0.18 in) toe-in

Setting... 1.0 to 3.0 mm (0.04 to 0.12 in) toe-in

Nominal castor angle (non-adjustable):

	Saloon/Hatchback	Estate
Domestic....................................	1°52'	1°44'
Domestic Nivomat........................	–	1°42'
Heavy duty	1°53'	1°58'
Heavy duty Nivomat.....................	–	1°42'
Business	–	1°43'

Nominal camber angle non-adjustable:

Domestic....................................	0°21'	0°25'
Domestic Nivomat........................	–	0°25'
Heavy duty	0°04'	0°06'
Heavy duty Nivomat.....................		0°06'
Business	–	0°26'

Granada (up to 1985):

Toe setting:

Checking .... 2.0 mm (0.078 in) toe-out to 5.0 mm (0.196 in) toe-in

Setting... 1.5 mm (0.06 in) toe-in

Castor angle .... 2°0' (+1°0'/–0°45')

Nominal camber angle .... 0°24' (+0°45'/–0°45')

Maximum allowable difference between left and right-hand sides:

Castor... 0°45'

Camber .... 1°0'

Granada (1986 on):

Toe setting

Setting valve... 1.0 to 3.0 mm (0.04 to 0.12 in) toe-in

Tolerance in service... 0.5 mm (0.02 in) toe-out to 4.5 mm (0.18 in) toe-in

Nominal castor angle non-adjustable:

Standard (without ride height control)................. 1°51'

Standard (with ride height control)..................... 1°58'

Heavy duty .... 1°46'

Front wheel alignment (continued)
Nominal camber angle non-adjustable:
    Standard (with/without ride height control) .... 0°23′
    Heavy duty.. 0°0′
Maximum allowable difference between left and right-hand sides:
    Castor .... 1°0′
    Camber .... 1°15′

Steering
Number of turns lock-to-lock:
  Sierra:
    Manual steering... 4.20
    Cam Gears power steering 2.71
    ZF power steering 2.56
  Granada (up to 1985):
    Manual steering... Not specified
    Power steering 3.50
  Granada (1986 on) 2.63
Power steering fluid type .... ATF to Ford spec SQM-2C 9010-A (Duckhams Uni-Matic or D-Matic)

Tyre pressures – bar (lbf/in²)

	Front	Rear
Sierra (Saloon/Hatchback):		
165 R 13 tyres:		
Normal use	1.8 (26)	1.8 (26)
Laden	2.0 (29)	2.5 (36)
185/70 R 13-T tyres:		
Normal use	1.8 (26)	1.8 (26)
Laden	2.0 (29)	2.5 (36)
Sierra (Estate):		
175 R 13 tyres:		
Normal use	1.8 (26)	1.8 (26)
Laden	2.0 (29)	3.3 (48)
Granada (up to 1985):		
185 SR 14 tyres:		
Normal use	2.1 (30)	1.7 (25)
Laden	2.1 (30)	2.5 (36)
Granada (1986 on):		
185 TR 14 tyres:		
Normal use	1.8 (26)	1.8 (26)
Laden	2.1 (30)	3.1 (45)

Torque wrench settings – suspension

	Nm	lbf ft
Front suspension		
Sierra:		
Anti-roll bar clamp bolts	57 to 70	42 to 52
Anti-roll bar-to-lower arm bolts	70 to 110	52 to 81
Front suspension arm lower pivot nut:		
Stage 1	45	33
Slacken off completely, then Stage 2	15	11
Stage 3	Tighten through a further 90°	
Crossmember bolts	70 to 90	52 to 66
Hub retaining nut	310 to 350	229 to 258
Lower arm balljoint	65 to 85	48 to 63
Strut upper mounting nut	40 to 52	29 to 38
Strut to spindle	80 to 90	59 to 66
Granada (up to 1985):		
Sub-frame-to-body bolts	80 to 100	59 to 77
Tie bar front bush nuts	60 to 70	44 to 52
Upper arm pivot bolts	90 to 120	66 to 88
Lower arm-to-sub-frame bolts	85 to 95	63 to 70
Anti-roll bar clamp bolts	17 to 24	13 to 18
Engine mounting nuts	41 to 51	30 to 45
Stub axle balljoints:		
Stage 1	41 to 51	30 to 45
Stage 2	58 to 89	43 to 66
Tie-bar-to-lower arm	58 to 68	43 to 50
Shock absorber upper mounting	38 to 47	28 to 35
Shock absorber lower mounting	8 to 12	6 to 9
Anti-roll bar-to-connecting link bolts	10 to 12	7 to 9
Granada (from 1986):		
Hub nut	390 to 450	288 to 332
Lower arm balljoint nut	65 to 85	48 to 63
Top mount retaining nuts	20 to 24	15 to 18
Stub axle carrier pinch-bolt	80 to 90	59 to 66
Anti-roll bar clamps	70 to 90	52 to 66

Torque wrench settings (continued)

	Nm	lbf ft
Anti-roll bar-to-lower arms	70 to 110	52 to 81
Crossmember-to-frame bolts	70 to 90	52 to 66
Suspension strut-to-turret nuts	40 to 52	30 to 38
Lower arm pivot:		
Stage 1 (clamping)	45	33
Slacken, then Stage 2 (snug)	15	11
Stage 3	Tighten 90° further	Tighten 90° further

Rear suspension

Granada (up to 1985):

	Nm	lbf ft
Axle mounting castellated nut	172 to 210	123 to 151
Crossmember-to-body centre bolt	68 to 88	50 to 63
Crossmember-to-body bracket bolts	40 to 50	29 to 36
Suspension arm-to-crossmember bolts	68 to 88	50 to 63
Shock absorber-to-suspension arm mounting	40 to 50	29 to 36
Shock absorber-to-body mounting	25 to 35	18 to 25

Granada (1986 on) and Sierra:

	Nm	lbf ft
Guide plate-to-floor bolts	41 to 51	30 to 38
Guide plate insulator bolt	69 to 88	51 to 65
Lower arm-to-crossmember bolt	80 to 95	59 to 70
Brake anchor plate to lower arm	52 to 64	38 to 47
Anti-roll bar bracket bolts	20 to 25	15 to 18
Shock absorber mountings:		
Top	73 to 97	54 to 72
Bottom	68 to 92	50 to 68
Rear hub bolts	80 to 100	59 to 74

All models:

	Nm	lbf ft
Road wheel bolts	70 to 100	52 to 74

Torque wrench settings – steering

Manual steering

Sierra:

	Nm	lbf ft
Steering gear-to-crossmember bolts:		
Stage 1	45	33
Stage 2	Refer to text for details	
Track-rod end-to-steering arm	25 to 30	18 to 22
Track-rod end locknut	57 to 68	42 to 50
Steering arm inner balljoint	100 to 120	74 to 89
Pinion shaft cover nut	70 to 100	52 to 74
Coupling shaft-to-column shaft bolts	20 to 25	15 to 18
Coupling shaft-to-pinion pinch-bolt	20 to 30	15 to 22
Steering wheel-to-column shaft nut	45 to 66	33 to 41
Slipper yoke plug:		
Stage 1	4 to 5	3 to 3.5
Stage 2	Loosen 60° to 70°	

Granada (up to 1985):

	Nm	lbf ft
Steering gear-to-sub-frame	22 to 30	16 to 22
Track-rod end-to-steering arm	25 to 30	18 to 22
Coupling-to-pinion spline bolt	17 to 20	12 to 15
Coupling unit-to-steering column shaft bolts	17 to 20	12 to 15
Steering wheel to column shaft nut	45 to 55	33 to 41
Track rod end locknut	57 to 68	42 to 50
Track rod end balljoint	45 to 51	33 to 37
Pinion preload cover bolts	17 to 24	13 to 17
Rack slipper cover bolts	17 to 24	13 to 17
Pinion turning torque	0.6 to 2.0	5 to 18 lbf in

Cam Gears type power steering

Granada (up to 1985):

	Nm	lbf ft
Steering coupling clamp bolts	16 to 20	12 to 15
Steering coupling pinch-bolts	16 to 20	12 to 15
Yoke cover plate	10 to 12	7 to 9
Torx screws	5.5 to 7	4 to 5
Quick-fit connector coupling	20 to 27	15 to 20
Pressure host-to-pump union	26 to 31	19 to 22
Return hose-to-pump union	16 to 20	12 to 15
Pulley hub bolt	10 to 12	7 to 9
Rack-to-crossmember bolts	22 to 30	16 to 22
Column clamp and brace nuts	17 to 24	13 to 17
Track-rod end-to-steering arm	25 to 30	18 to 22
Track-rod end locknut	57 to 68	42 to 50

Torque wrench settings – steering (continued)

	Nm	lbf ft
Granada (1986 on) and Sierra:		
Steering coupling clamp bolt	17 to 20	13 to 15
Steering coupling pinch-bolts	17 to 20	12 to 15
Lower pinion nut	37 to 47	27 to 35
Track-rod end locknuts	57 to 68	42 to 50
Track-rod end-to-steering arm	25 to 30	18 to 22
Steering arm inner balljoint	70 to 77	52 to 57
Pressure hose-to-pump union	26 to 31	19 to 22
Pulley hub nut	10 to 12	7 to 9
Steering column clamp and brace nuts	17 to 24	13 to 17
Power steering pump support-to-engine	52 to 64	38 to 47
Steering gear-to-crossmember bolts:		
Stage 1	15	11
Stage 2	Tighten further 90°	
ZF type power steering (where different to Cam Gears type)		
Granada (up to 1985):		
Rack yoke cover plate	22 to 24	16 to 17
Allen screws	15 to 19	11 to 14
Track-rod inner balljoint	70 to 72	52 to 56
Rack tube-to-pinion housing	120 to 130	89 to 96
Drivebelt tension adjuster bolt locknut	20 to 25	15 to 18
Pulley-to-pump bolt	20 to 25	15 to 18
Granada (1986 on) and Sierra:		
Rack yoke cover plate	7 to 8	5 to 6
Steering arm inner balljoint	72 to 88	53 to 65

1 General description

1 The suspension and steering systems on the Diesel engine models are in general identical to the equivalent petrol engine models. Some components do differ to suit the Diesel engine variants. For example, the power steering pump drivebelt on the earlier Granada (up to 1985) model is driven from the crankshaft pulley and adjusted by an idler pulley. Also on that model, the fluid reservoir for the power steering system is mounted separately on the left-hand inner wing panel.

2 The inspection, maintenance and repair procedures are as described for the equivalent petrol engine model and reference to the appropriate model-specific workshop manual will therefore be necessary. However, refer to the Specifications at the start of this Chapter for the model in question, as some of the specification data for the diesel variants do differ.

2 Power steering system (all models) – bleeding

1 When bleeding the power steering system first disconnect the fuel cut-off solenoid lead to prevent the engine from starting as it is cranked over.

2 The system can now be bled as described in the appropriate model-specific workshop manual, but ignore the reference to detaching the ignition coil low tension negative lead (where given).

3 When the system is bled, reconnect the fuel cut-off solenoid lead.

3 Steering gear (Sierra and 1986 on Granada) – removal, overhaul and refitting

1 The removal, overhaul and refitting procedures are in general the same as described for the petrol engine models, but reference must be made to the Specifications at the start of this Chapter for data applicable to the Diesel engine models.

2 When removing the steering gear on diesel engine models it will also be necessary to detach and remove the engine undertray for access to the steering gear mountings and associated components.

3 When refitting the manual steering gear unit and tightening the steering gear-to-crossmember retaining bolts, tighten them to the specified clamping torque (Stage 1) then loosen them off the point where they are free of torque. From this point retighten them to a 'snug' torque of 15 Nm (11 lbf ft) then tighten them a further 90° from that point. DO NOT overtighten the bolts beyond this point or the bolts (which are of the torque yield type) will be weakened. If the bolts are to be checked for tightness at any time, loosen them off then tighten them through the stages as described.

4 Wheels and tyres – general care and maintenance

Wheels and tyres should give no real problems in use provided that a close eye is kept on them with regard to excessive wear or damage. To this end, the following points should be noted.

Ensure that tyre pressures are checked regularly and maintained correctly. Checking should be carried out with the tyres cold and not immediately after the vehicle has been in use. If the pressures are checked with the tyres hot, an apparently high reading will be obtained owing to heat expansion. Under no circumstances should an attempt be made to reduce the pressures to the quoted cold reading in this instance, or effective underinflation will result.

Underinflation will cause overheating of the tyre owing to excessive flexing of the casing, and the tread will not sit correctly on the road surface. This will cause a consequent loss of adhesion and excessive wear, not to mention the danger of sudden tyre failure due to heat build-up.

Overinflation will cause rapid wear of the centre part of the tyre tread coupled with reduced adhesion, harsher ride, and the danger of shock damage occurring in the tyre casing.

Regularly check the tyres for damage in the form of cuts or bulges, especially in the sidewalls. Remove any nails or stones embedded in the tread before they penetrate the tyre to cause deflation. If removal of a nail *does* reveal that the tyre has been punctured, refit the nail so that its point of penetration is marked. Then immediately change the wheel and have the tyre repaired by a tyre dealer. Do *not* drive on a tyre in such a condition. In many cases a puncture can be simply repaired by the use of an inner tube of the correct size and type. If in any doubt as to the possible consequences of any damage found, consult your local tyre dealer for advice.

Periodically remove the wheels and clean any dirt or mud from the inside and outside surfaces. Examine the wheel rims for signs of rusting, corrosion or other damage. Light alloy wheels are easily damaged by 'kerbing' whilst parking, and similarly steel wheels may become dented or buckled. Renewal of the wheel is very often the only course of remedial action possible.

The balance of each wheel and tyre assembly should be maintained to avoid excessive wear, not only to the tyres but also to the steering and suspension components. Wheel imbalance is normally signified by vibration through the vehicle's bodyshell, although in many cases it is particularly noticeable through the steering wheel. Conversely, it should be noted that wear or damage in suspension or steering components may cause excessive tyre wear. Out-of-round or out-of-true tyres, damaged wheels and wheel bearing wear/maladjustment also fall into this category. Balancing will not usually cure vibration caused by such wear.

Wheel balancing may be carried out with the wheel either on or off the vehicle. If balanced on the vehicle, ensure that the wheel-to-hub relationship is marked in some way prior to subsequent wheel removal so that it may be refitted in its original position.

General tyre wear is influenced to a large degree by driving style harsh braking and acceleration or fast cornering will all produce more rapid tyre wear. Interchanging of tyres may result in more even wear, but this should only be carried out where there is no mix of tyre types on the vehicle. However, it is worth bearing in mind that if this is completely effective, the added expense of replacing a complete set of tyres simultaneously is incurred, which may prove financially restrictive for many owners.

Front tyres may wear unevenly as a result of wheel misalignment. The front wheels should always be correctly aligned according to the settings specified by the vehicle manufacturer.

Legal restrictions apply to the mixing of tyre types on a vehicle. Basically this means that a vehicle must not have tyres of differing construction on the same axle. Although it is not recommended to mix tyre types between front axle and rear axle, the only legally permissible combination is crossply at the front and radial at the rear. When mixing radial ply tyres, textile braced radials must always go on the front axle, with steel braced radials at the rear. An obvious disadvantage of such mixing is the necessity to carry two spare tyres to avoid contravening the law in the event of a puncture.

In the UK, the Motor Vehicles Construction and Use Regulations apply to many aspects of tyre fitting and usage. It is suggested that a copy of these regulations is obtained from your local police if in doubt as to the current legal requirements with regard to tyre condition, minimum tread depth, etc.

Chapter 8 Electrical system

Contents

Specifications

General
System type .... 12 volt, negative earth
Battery... Lead-acid, 12 volt

Alternator
Type.. Bosch, Lucas or Motorola
Output .... 70 amp
Minimum allowable brush length .... 5 mm (0.197 in)

Starter motor
Type/make .... Pre-engaged, Bosch
Rating .... 2.0 kW
Armature endfloat.. 0.3 mm (0.01 in)
Minimum allowable brush length .... 10.0 mm (0.39 in)

---

1 General description and cautionary notes

1   The electrical system is of 12 volt negative earth type. The main components are a 12 volt battery, an alternator with integral voltage regulator, and a pre-engaged starter motor. The starter motor incor-porates a one-way clutch on its pinion shaft to prevent the engine driving the motor when it starts.

2   It is important to disconnect the battery earth (negative) lead before charging the battery, removing the alternator, or working on any wiring circuits which are permanently live (photos). Additionally, the alternator

1.2A Battery earth (negative) lead connection (Turbo shown)

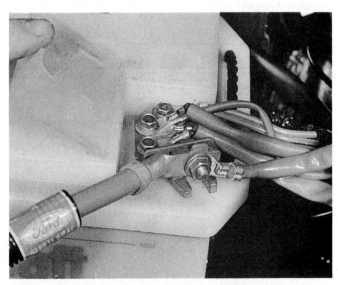

1.2B Battery positive lead connection (Turbo shown)

3.2 Alternator lead connections on rear face

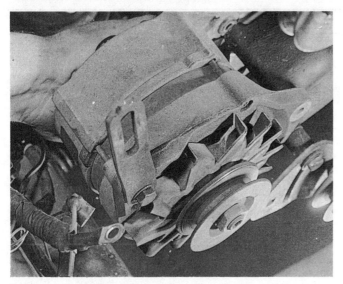

3.4B ... and lift the alternator clear (Sierra shown)

3.4A Remove the adjuster and pivot bolts ...

5   Refitting is a reversal of the removal procedure, but when the drivebelt is engaged in the alternator pulley, adjust its tension as described in Chapter 2. Ensure that the wiring connections are clean and secure.

4   Alternator – brush renewal

1   Remove the alternator unit as described in the previous Section.

2   Undo the voltage regulator/brush unit retaining screws and withdraw the combined unit from the rear face of the alternator (photos).

3   Measure the length of brushes protruding from the holder. If they are at or under the minimum allowable length, renew the unit complete (photo).

4   Before refitting, clean the slip rings with a petrol-moistened cloth.

5   Relocate the unit into position so that the brushes engage over the clip rings, then secure with the screws. Refit the alternator unit.

wiring must also be disconnected before using an electric arc welder to carry out any repairs to the car's bodywork.

2   Routine maintenance

The procedures are as described for petrol engine models, but refer to Chapter 2 in this manual for details describing the alternator drivebelt tension check, adjustment and renewal.

3   Alternator – removal and refitting

1   Disconnect the battery earth (negative) lead.

2   Detach the wires from the rear of the alternator (photo).

3   Loosen the alternator pivot and adjuster bolts then swivel the alternator towards the engine to loosen off the drivebelt tension. Disengage the drivebelt from the alternator pulley.

4   Unscrew the adjuster and pivot bolts then lift the alternator unit from the engine (photos).

4.2A Undo the retaining screws (arrowed) ...

4.2B ... and lift the voltage regulator/brush unit from the alternator

4.3 General view showing brushes

5.4 Disconnect the wiring from the starter motor

5.7 Removing the starter motor from the 2.3 litre engine (oil cooler pipes removed)

8   Refitting is a reversal of the removal procedure. Ensure that the wiring connections are securely and cleanly made.

---

5   Starter motor – removal and refitting

---

1   Disconnect the battery earth (negative) lead.

2   Raise the car at the front end and support it on axle stands.

3   Detach and remove the engine undertray (where fitted).

4   Disconnect the wiring from the starter motor (photo).

5   Undo the starter motor-to-engine/transmission housing retaining bolts and, where applicable, detach the engine earth lead from the upper retaining bolt.

6   Where applicable, undo the retaining bolts and detach the support bracket from the underside of the starter motor.

7   Withdraw and remove the starter motor unit (photo). If a long case starter motor is fitted it will be necessary to unbolt the left-hand engine mounting and move it out of the way. If this is necessary, first support the weight of the engine with a hoist or jack.

---

6   Starter motor – overhaul

---

1   Before embarking on a major overhaul of a starter motor, check the availability of spare parts and compare their cost with that of a new cr reconditioned motor.

2   Remove the starter motor as described in the previous Section. Where applicable, remove the rear support bracket.

3   Disconnect the motor lead from the solenoid terminal.

4   Remove the two screws which secure the armature end cap. Remove the cap, the C-washer, the plain washer(s) and cap seal (photos).

5   Remove the two through-bolts or studs. If the stud nuts are inaccessible, lock two nuts together on the stud and turn them to unscrew it.

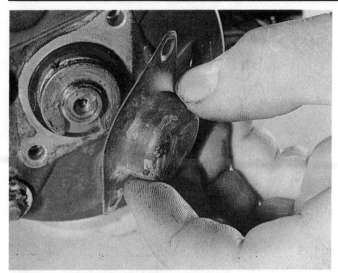

6.4A Remove the starter motor end cap ...

6.4B ... withdraw the C-washer ...

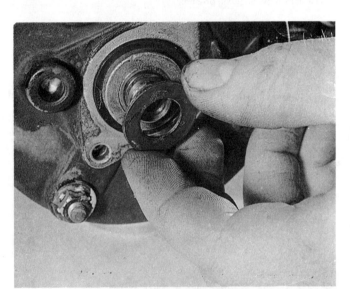

6.4C ... plain washer ...

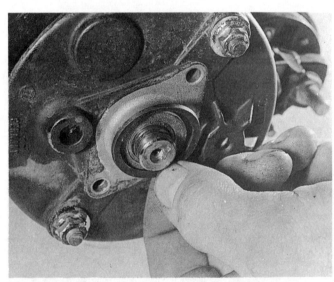

6.4D ... and cap seal

6.6 Starter motor end cover removed to show the brush gear unit

6   Remove the commutator end cover to expose the brushgear (photo). Carefully withdraw the brushplate from the commutator. Be careful to avoid damage to the brushes as they are released.

7   Examine the brushes: they should not be excessively worn (see Specifications) and must slide freely in their holders. Brush renewal varies according to motor type as follows:

   Short frame – the brush lead must be removed from the stand-off connector on the brushplate, and the clip on the new brush lead be soldered to the connector (Fig. 8.3)
   Long frame – the old brush leads must be cut and the new leads attached by soldering

8   Remove the two or three screws which secure the solenoid to the drive end housing. Withdraw the solenoid yoke and unhook and remove the plunger. Note the location of springs, washers etc.

9   Remove the field winding yoke, if necessary tapping the drive end housing off it.

10   Remove the armature pinion and actuating lever from the drive end housing. On the long frame motor the actuating lever is secured by a pivot nut and bolt; on the other motors it is secured by a rubber plug.

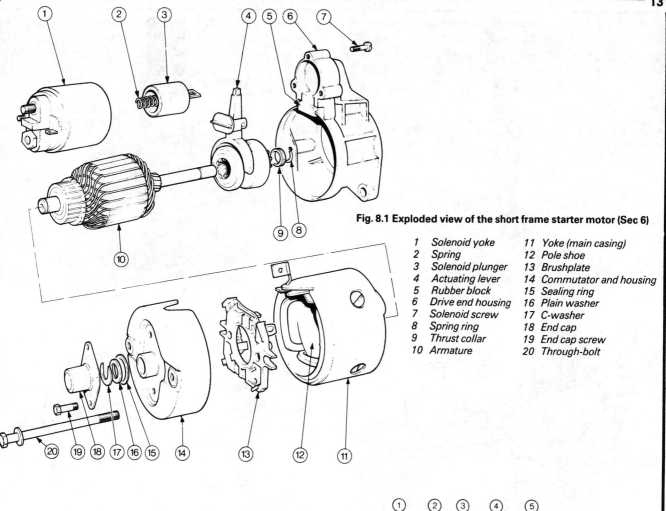

Fig. 8.1 Exploded view of the short frame starter motor (Sec 6)

1	Solenoid yoke	11	Yoke (main casing)
2	Spring	12	Pole shoe
3	Solenoid plunger	13	Brushplate
4	Actuating lever	14	Commutator and housing
5	Rubber block	15	Sealing ring
6	Drive end housing	16	Plain washer
7	Solenoid screw	17	C-washer
8	Spring ring	18	End cap
9	Thrust collar	19	End cap screw
10	Armature	20	Through-bolt

Fig. 8.2 Exploded view of the long frame starter motor (Sec 6)

1 Solenoid
2 Gasket
3 Switch contacts
4 Terminals
5 Screw
6 End cap
7 Seal
8 C-washer
9 Plain washers
10 Bush
11 Commutator end housing
12 Brushplate
13 Connector link
14 Yoke (main casing)
15 Drive end housing
16 Solenoid screw
17 Bush
18 Pivot bolt
19 Actuating lever
20 Through-bolt
21 Brush spring
22 Brush
23 Commutator
24 Armature
25 Pinion and clutch
26 Thrust collar
27 Spring ring

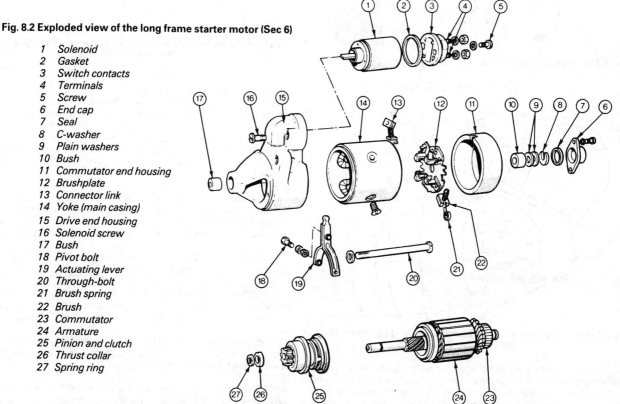

6.11 Using a tube and hammer to drive down the thrust collar (typical)

6.16 Levering the collar up over the spring clip (typical)

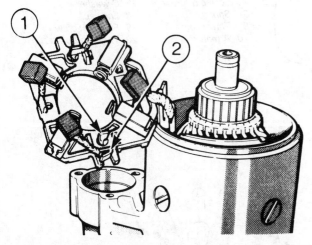

Fig. 8.3 Brushplate and brushes – short frame starter motor (Sec 6)

1   Stand-off connector   2   Clip

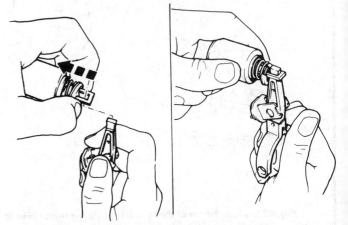

Fig. 8.4 Fitting the solenoid plunger to the actuating lever – short frame motor (Sec 6)

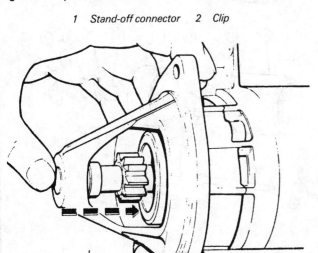

Fig. 8.5 Push the armature in the direction arrowed before checking the endfloat (Sec 6)

11   To remove the pinion and one-way clutch from the armature, carefully grip the armature (**not** the clutch) in a vice with padded jaws. Use a tube and hammer to drive the thrust collar down the shaft to expose the spring ring. Remove the spring ring and the thrust collar, then pull off the clutch and pinion (photo).

12   Inspect all components for wear and damage. The armature shaft bushes can be renewed if necessary. If there are signs that the armature has been touching pole pieces, bush wear may be suspected.

13   Simple continuity checks can be made on the armature and (when applicable) the field windings, using a multi-meter or a battery and test lamp. Special test equipment is required for thorough checking, however.

14   A burnt or otherwise damaged commutator can sometimes be reclaimed by machining, providing that the refinishing limit is not exceeded. This is specialist work. Beware of using abrasives to clean the commutator, as particles may become embedded in the copper.

15   Renew of individual field coils or magnets is not possible without special equipment, even if the parts are available.

16   Commence reassembly by fitting the clutch and pinion to the armature. Fit the thrust collar and a new spring clip to the shaft, then use a couple of spanners to lever the collar over the clip (photo).

17   Reassemble the motor in the reverse order to that followed when dismantling. Note how the solenoid plunger is fitted to the actuating lever on the short frame motor (Fig. 8.4).

18   Clean the commutator with a rag moistened with methylated spirit, then refit the brushplate. Either clip the brushes in place after fitting the plate, or use a tube of suitable diameter to keep the brushes

7.3 Glow plug/temperature warning lamps and cubby removal – Sierra

7.5 Glow plug/temperature warning lamp and bulb holder connections on rear face – Sierra

retracted during fitting. Make sure that the brushplate is correctly positioned to allow the passage of through-bolts or studs.

19   Adjust the armature endfloat when refitting the plain end C-washers. Add or subtract plain washers so that the endfloat is as near zero as possible, without preloading. Push the armature towards the commutator end to take up any slack before checking the endfloat.

20   Apply a little grease to the armature end before refitting the cap.

21   If a rear support bracket is fitted, only tighten its securing nuts loosely until after the motor has been refitted to the vehicle.

---

7   Glow plugs warning lamp and relay – removal and refitting

1   Disconnect the battery earth (negative) lead.

Glow plugs
2   Refer to Chapter 3 in this manual for the removal and refitting procedures of the glow plugs.

Glow plug warning lamp
3   On Sierra models, grip the cubby panel with the fingers and pull it free from the facia together with the glow plug and engine temperature warning lamps (photo).

4   On early Granada models (up to 1985), the glow plug warning lamp also serves as an engine temperature warning. Located in the instrument panel, its removal and refitting procedures are as described for the panel switches in the model-specific owners workshop manual.

5   To remove either warning lamp unit from the panel, detach the wire and release the unit securing clips. To inspect/renew the warning lamp bulb, withdraw the holder and extract the bulb from it (photo).

7.8 Glow plug relay unit location. Pull back the rubber gaiter for access to the wiring connection

6   Refit in the reverse order of removal.

7   On later Granada models (1985 on), the glow plug warning lamp is located in the instrument cluster, the removal and dismantling of which are described in the model-specific owners workshop manual.

Glow plug relay
8   This is located in the engine compartment on the left-hand side near the fuel filter. To remove the relay, detach the wiring connector, undo the retaining screw and withdraw the relay from the filter support bracket (photo).

9   Refit in the reverse order of removal.

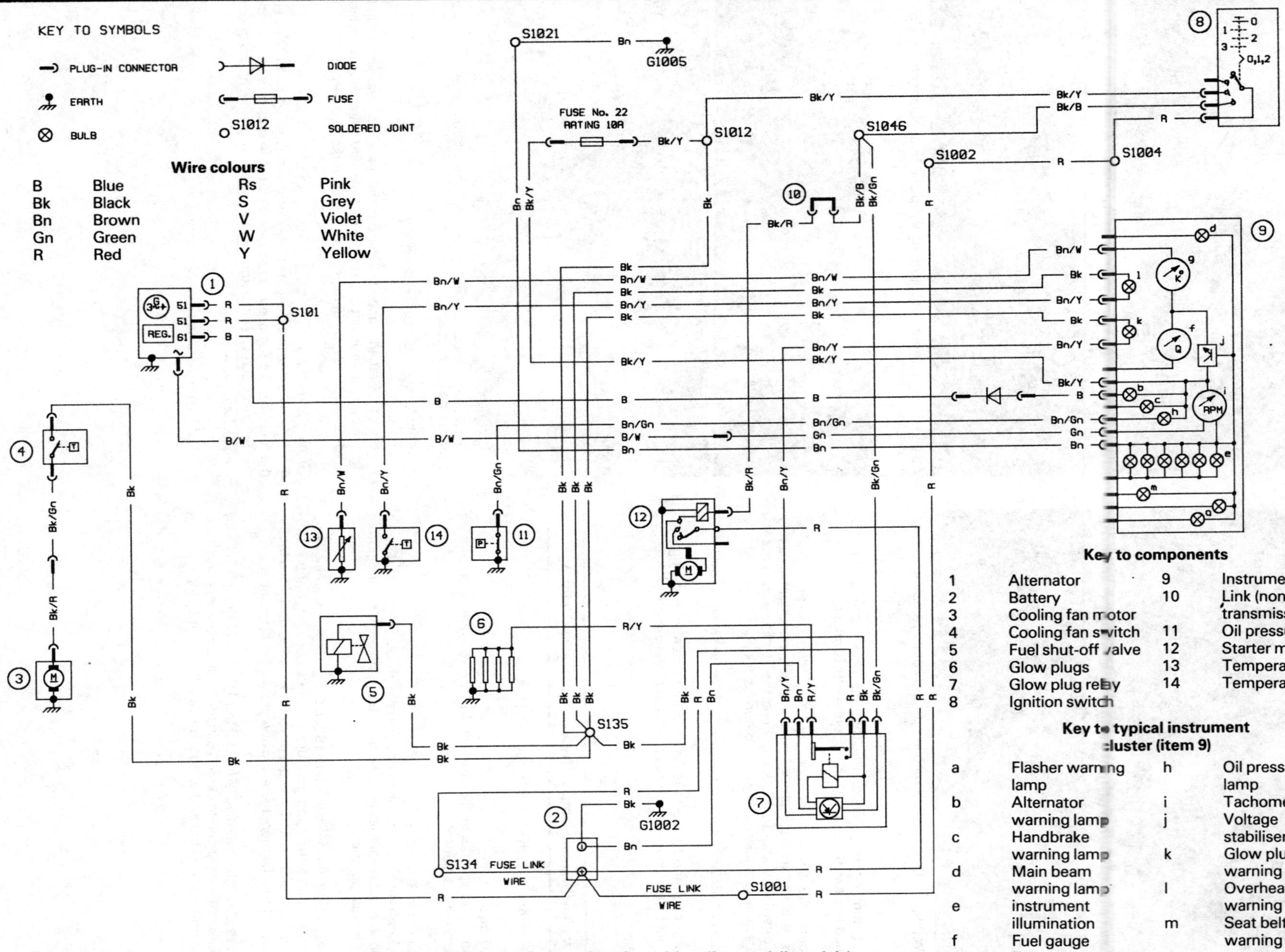
KEY TO SYMBOLS
PLUG-IN CONNECTOR
EARTH
BULB
DIODE
FUSE
S1012
SOLDERED JOINT
S1021
G1005
FUSE No. 22
RATING 10A
S1012
S1046
S1002
S1004
S101
S135
S134
FUSE LINK
WIRE
S1001
G1002
REG.
RPM

Wire colours

B	Blue	Rs	Pink
Bk	Black	S	Grey
Bn	Brown	V	Violet
Gn	Green	W	White
R	Red	Y	Yellow

Starting, charging and general engine wiring diagram (all models)

Key to components

1	Alternator	9	Instrument cluster
2	Battery	10	Link (non-automatic transmission)
3	Cooling fan motor	11	Oil pressure switch
4	Cooling fan switch	12	Starter motor
5	Fuel shut-off valve	13	Temperature sender
6	Glow plugs	14	Temperature switch
7	Glow plug relay		
8	Ignition switch		

Key to typical instrument cluster (item 9)

a	Flasher warning lamp	h	Oil pressure lamp
b	Alternator warning lamp	i	Tachometer
c	Handbrake warning lamp	j	Voltage stabiliser
d	Main beam warning lamp	k	Glow plug warning lamp
e	instrument illumination	l	Overheat warning lamp
f	Fuel gauge	m	Seat belt warning lamp
g	Temperature gauge		

Index